The KiDS' FUN-FILLED Search & Find GEOGRAPHY BOOK

By
Anthony Tallarico

ASIA, AUSTRALIA, AND ANTARCTICA

I

Search and find lots of interesting facts about:

- **Russia and the Commonwealth of Independent States**

- **China and Northeastern Asia**

- **Japan**

- **Southeast Asia**

- **Indonesia and the Island Nations**

- **The Indian Subcontinent**

- **The Middle East**

- **Turkey and Cyprus**

- **Australia and New Zealand**

- **Antarctica**

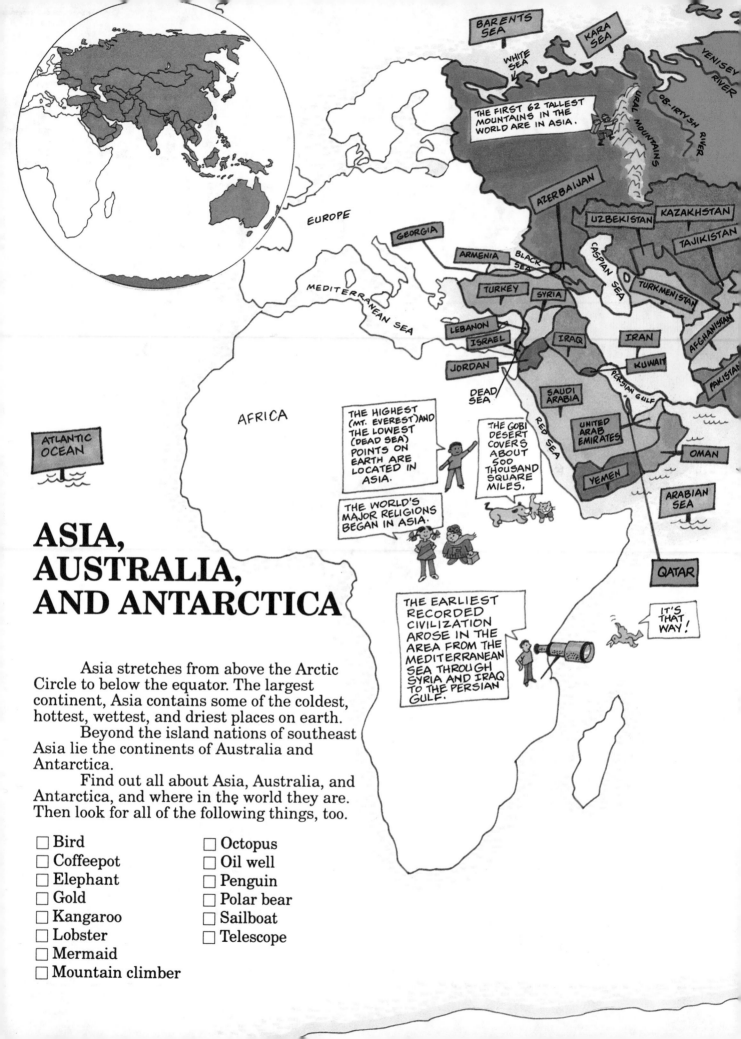

ASIA, AUSTRALIA, AND ANTARCTICA

Asia stretches from above the Arctic Circle to below the equator. The largest continent, Asia contains some of the coldest, hottest, wettest, and driest places on earth.

Beyond the island nations of southeast Asia lie the continents of Australia and Antarctica.

Find out all about Asia, Australia, and Antarctica, and where in the world they are. Then look for all of the following things, too.

☐ Bird
☐ Coffeepot
☐ Elephant
☐ Gold
☐ Kangaroo
☐ Lobster
☐ Mermaid
☐ Mountain climber
☐ Octopus
☐ Oil well
☐ Penguin
☐ Polar bear
☐ Sailboat
☐ Telescope

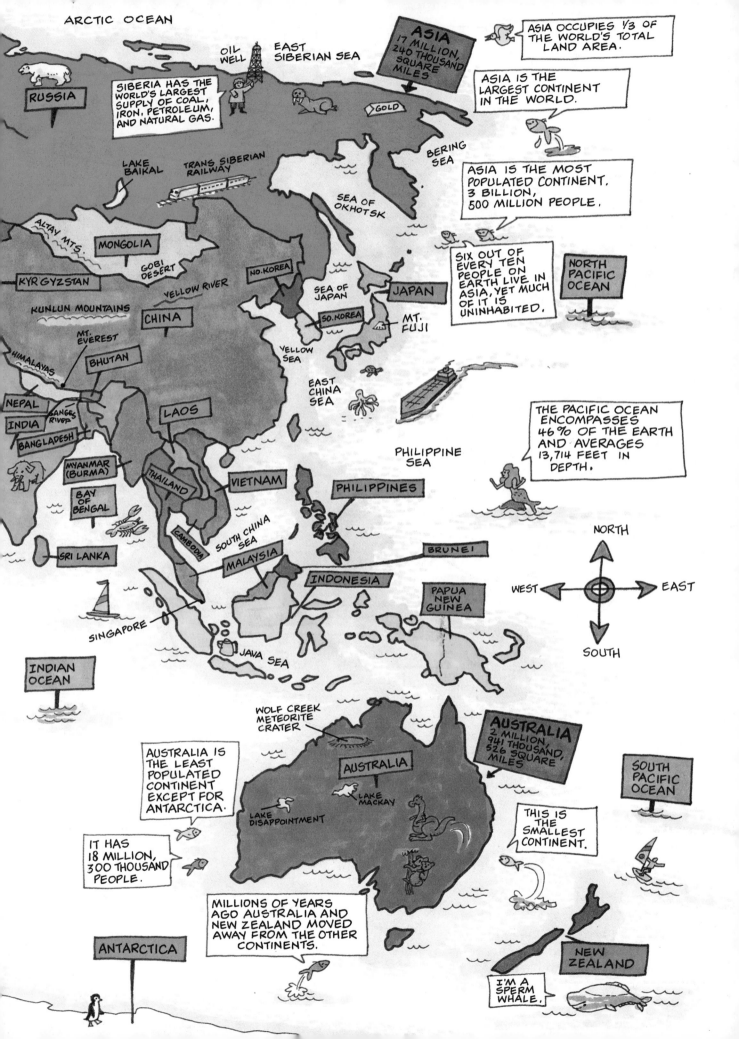

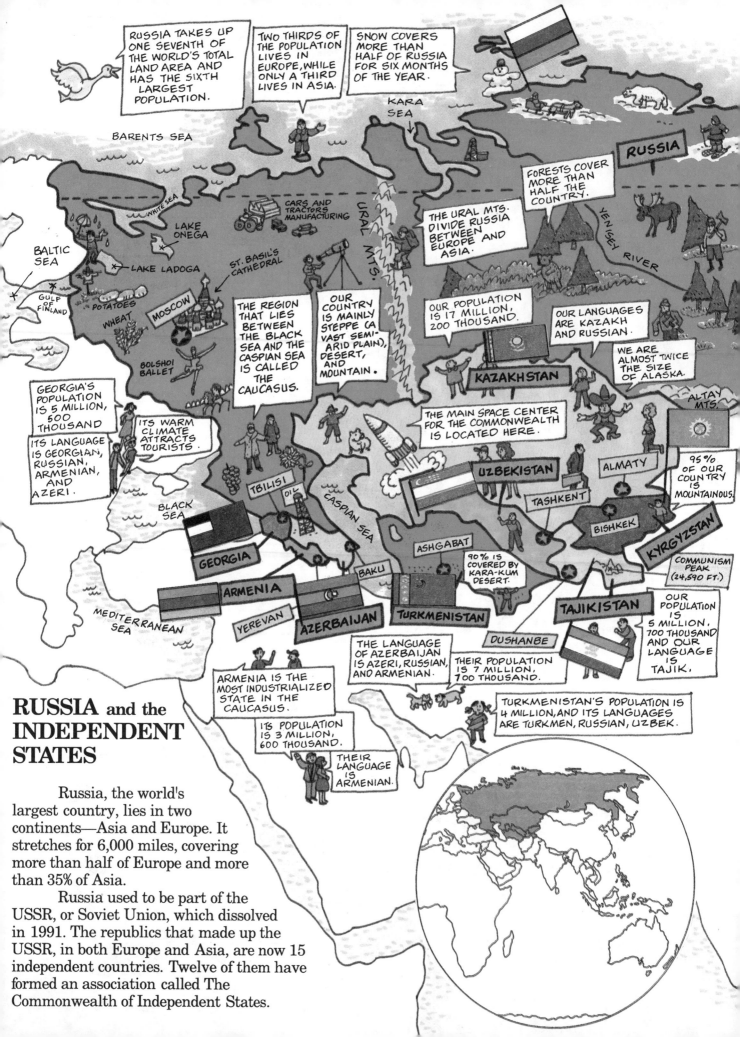

RUSSIA TAKES UP ONE SEVENTH OF THE WORLD'S TOTAL LAND AREA AND HAS THE SIXTH LARGEST POPULATION.

TWO THIRDS OF THE POPULATION LIVES IN EUROPE, WHILE ONLY A THIRD LIVES IN ASIA.

SNOW COVERS MORE THAN HALF OF RUSSIA FOR SIX MONTHS OF THE YEAR.

KARA SEA

BARENTS SEA

RUSSIA

FORESTS COVER MORE THAN HALF THE COUNTRY.

WHITE SEA

CARS AND TRACTORS MANUFACTURING

URAL MTS.

THE URAL MTS. DIVIDE RUSSIA BETWEEN EUROPE AND ASIA.

YENISEY RIVER

LAKE ONEGA

BALTIC SEA

LAKE LADOGA

ST. BASIL'S CATHEDRAL

OUR POPULATION IS 17 MILLION, 200 THOUSAND.

OUR LANGUAGES ARE KAZAKH AND RUSSIAN.

GULF OF FINLAND

POTATOES

WHEAT

MOSCOW

THE REGION THAT LIES BETWEEN THE BLACK SEA AND THE CASPIAN SEA IS CALLED THE CAUCASUS.

OUR COUNTRY IS MAINLY STEPPE (A VAST SEMI-ARID PLAIN), DESERT, AND MOUNTAIN.

WE ARE ALMOST TWICE THE SIZE OF ALASKA.

BOLSHOI BALLET

KAZAKHSTAN

ALTAY MTS.

GEORGIA'S POPULATION IS 5 MILLION, 500 THOUSAND

ITS WARM CLIMATE ATTRACTS TOURISTS.

THE MAIN SPACE CENTER FOR THE COMMONWEALTH IS LOCATED HERE.

ALMATY

ITS LANGUAGE IS GEORGIAN, RUSSIAN, ARMENIAN, AND AZERI.

UZBEKISTAN

95% OF OUR COUNTRY IS MOUNTAINOUS.

TBILISI

OIL

CASPIAN SEA

TASHKENT

BLACK SEA

BISHKEK

KYRGYZSTAN

ASHGABAT

COMMUNISM PEAK (24,590 FT.)

GEORGIA

BAKU

90% IS COVERED BY KARA-KUM DESERT.

TAJIKISTAN

OUR POPULATION IS 5 MILLION, 700 THOUSAND AND OUR LANGUAGE IS TAJIK.

ARMENIA

MEDITERRANEAN SEA

YEREVAN

AZERBAIJAN

TURKMENISTAN

DUSHANBE

THE LANGUAGE OF AZERBAIJAN IS AZERI, RUSSIAN, AND ARMENIAN.

THEIR POPULATION IS 7 MILLION, 700 THOUSAND.

TURKMENISTAN'S POPULATION IS 4 MILLION, AND ITS LANGUAGES ARE TURKMEN, RUSSIAN, UZBEK.

ARMENIA IS THE MOST INDUSTRIALIZED STATE IN THE CAUCASUS.

ITS POPULATION IS 3 MILLION, 600 THOUSAND.

THEIR LANGUAGE IS ARMENIAN.

RUSSIA and the INDEPENDENT STATES

Russia, the world's largest country, lies in two continents—Asia and Europe. It stretches for 6,000 miles, covering more than half of Europe and more than 35% of Asia.

Russia used to be part of the USSR, or Soviet Union, which dissolved in 1991. The republics that made up the USSR, in both Europe and Asia, are now 15 independent countries. Twelve of them have formed an association called The Commonwealth of Independent States.

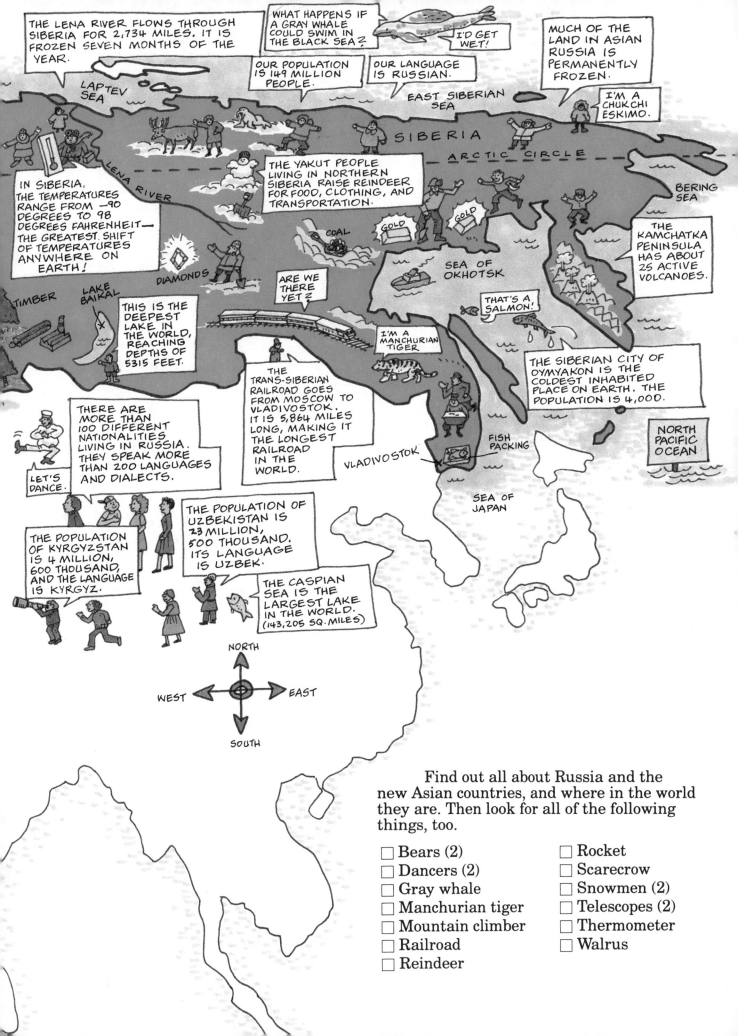

Find out all about Russia and the new Asian countries, and where in the world they are. Then look for all of the following things, too.

- ☐ Bears (2)
- ☐ Dancers (2)
- ☐ Gray whale
- ☐ Manchurian tiger
- ☐ Mountain climber
- ☐ Railroad
- ☐ Reindeer
- ☐ Rocket
- ☐ Scarecrow
- ☐ Snowmen (2)
- ☐ Telescopes (2)
- ☐ Thermometer
- ☐ Walrus

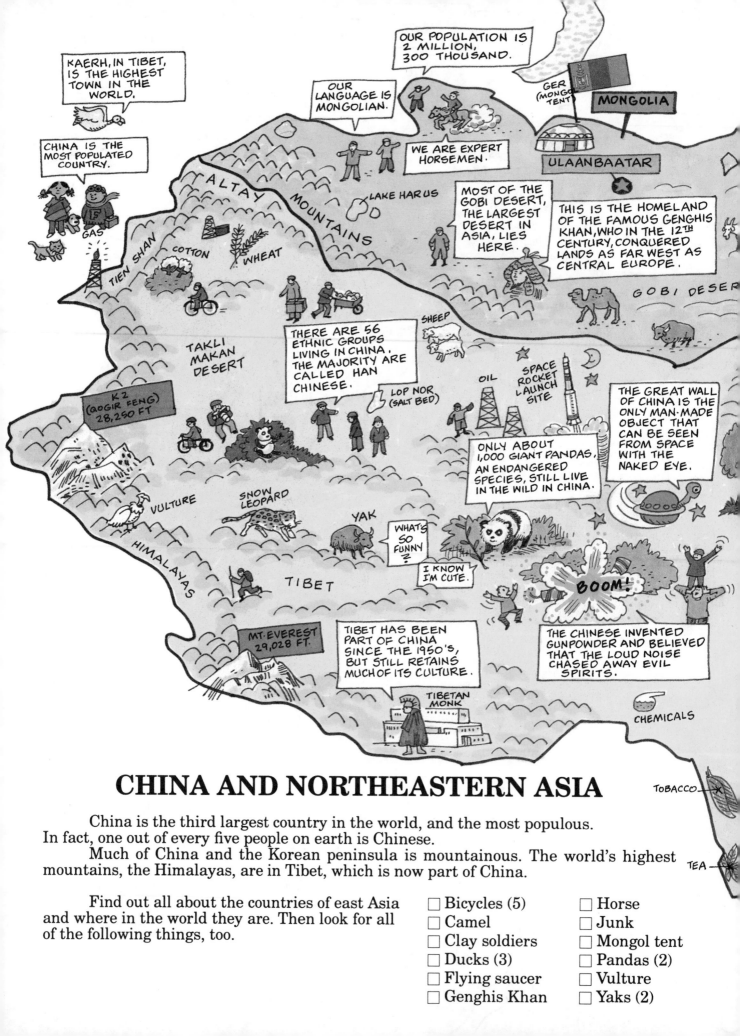

CHINA AND NORTHEASTERN ASIA

China is the third largest country in the world, and the most populous. In fact, one out of every five people on earth is Chinese.

Much of China and the Korean peninsula is mountainous. The world's highest mountains, the Himalayas, are in Tibet, which is now part of China.

Find out all about the countries of east Asia and where in the world they are. Then look for all of the following things, too.

- ☐ Bicycles (5)
- ☐ Camel
- ☐ Clay soldiers
- ☐ Ducks (3)
- ☐ Flying saucer
- ☐ Genghis Khan
- ☐ Horse
- ☐ Junk
- ☐ Mongol tent
- ☐ Pandas (2)
- ☐ Vulture
- ☐ Yaks (2)

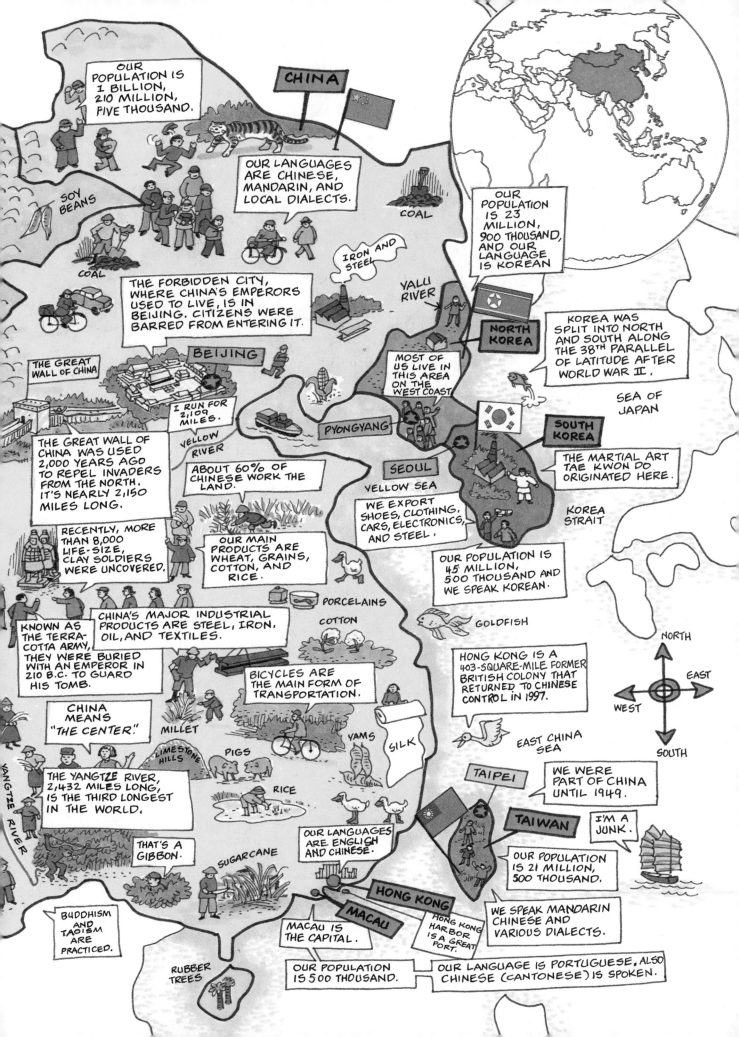

JAPAN

Japan consists of four main islands and about 4,000 smaller ones. This densely populated and leading industrial country is almost as large as California. Most of the people live in the big cities on Honshu Island and along the flat coastal areas.

Find out all about Japan and where in the world it is. Then look for all of the following things, too.

- ☐ Anchovies
- ☐ Baseball bat
- ☐ Brown bear
- ☐ Cod
- ☐ Cook
- ☐ Crab
- ☐ Cranes (2)
- ☐ Dollar sign
- ☐ Golfer
- ☐ Octopus
- ☐ Skier
- ☐ Snake
- ☐ Snow sculpture
- ☐ Squid
- ☐ Streamer
- ☐ Tofu
- ☐ Turtle
- ☐ Umbrellas (2)
- ☐ Wrestler

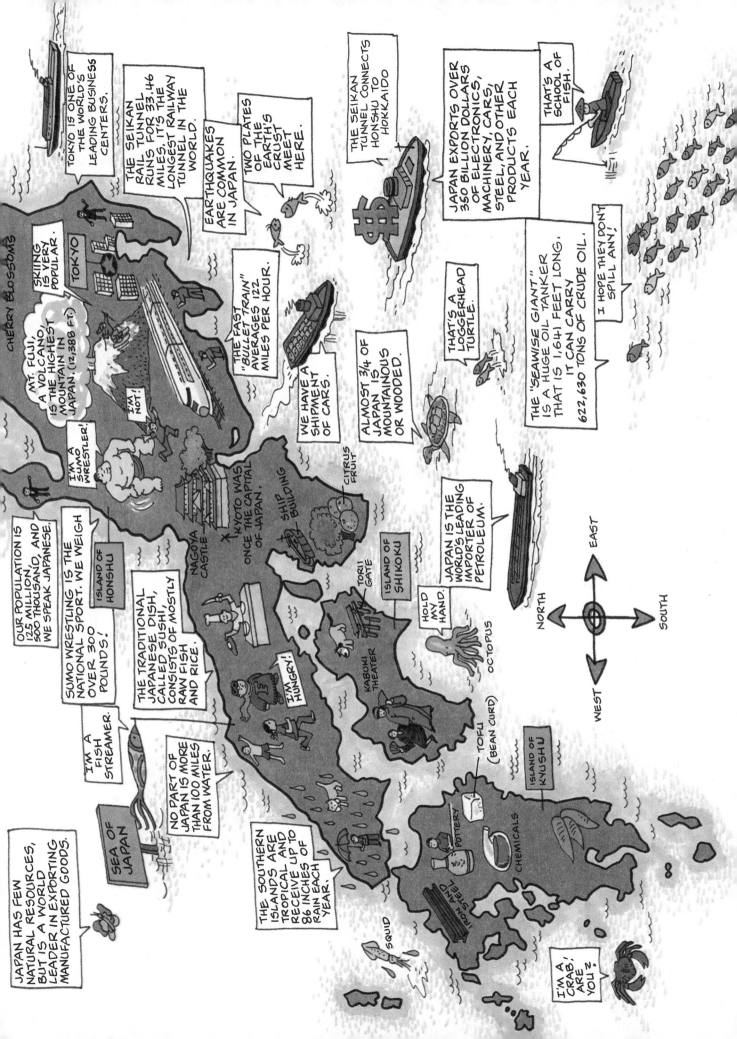

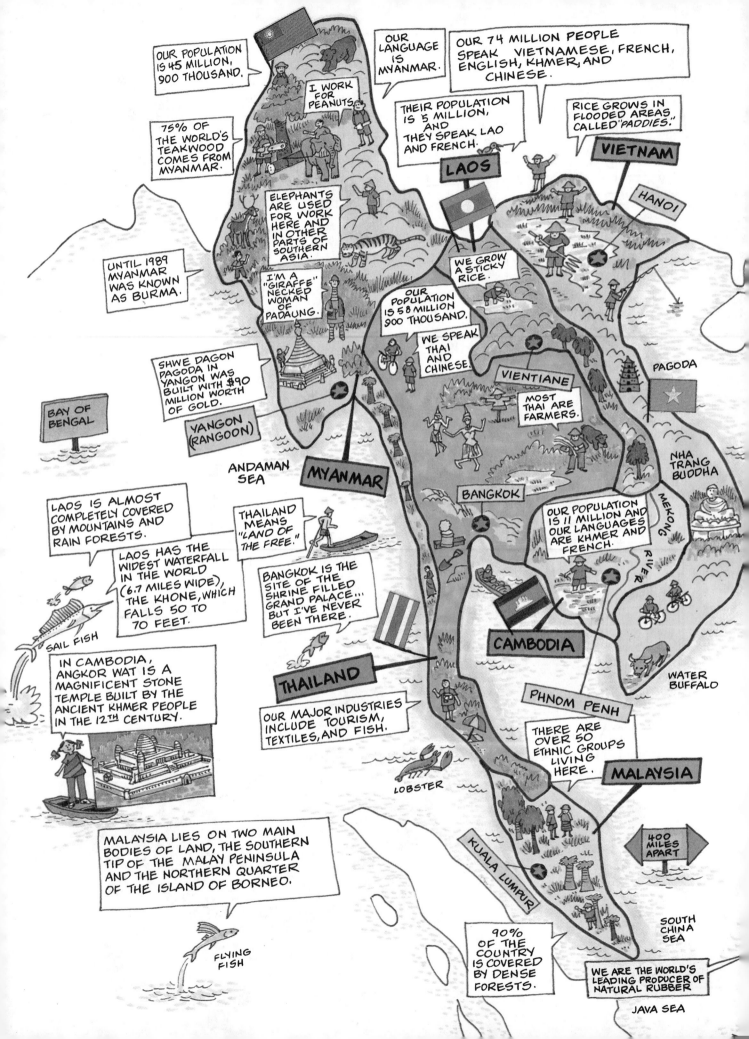

SOUTHEAST ASIA

Much of this region is covered with jungles, mountains, and rain forests. The Mekong River, 2,600 miles long, is the longest river in southeast Asia. It begins in the Himalayan Mountains, flows through five countries, and empties into the South China sea. Fifty million people depend on the river for irrigation, fish, and transportation.

Find out all about the countries of Southeast Asia and where in the world they are. Then look for all of the following things, too.

- ☐ Brown bears (2)
- ☐ Cyclists (3)
- ☐ Dancers
- ☐ Deer
- ☐ Elephant
- ☐ Fisherman
- ☐ Flying fish
- ☐ "Giraffe" neck
- ☐ Lobster
- ☐ Pitchfork
- ☐ Scarecrow
- ☐ Tiger
- ☐ Umbrellas (2)

MORE THAN 60% OF THE VIETNAMESE FARM OR FISH.

SOUTH CHINA SEA

VIETNAM HAS A VERY TROPICAL CLIMATE.

DURING THE MONSOON SEASON, STRONG WINDS AND HEAVY RAINS ARE COMMON, ESPECIALLY IN THE SOUTHERN REGIONS.

THEY HAVE ONLY TWO SEASONS — A WET, HOT SUMMER AND A COOL WINTER.

THE HEART OF CAMBODIA IS THE RIVER BASIN WATERED BY THE MEKONG RIVER.

THE MEKONG RIVER CREATES FERTILE FARMING AREAS WHERE MAINLY RICE AND CORN ARE GROWN.

NORTH
WEST EAST
SOUTH

MALAYSIA

BANDAR SERI BEGAWAN
THE SULTAN OF BRUNEI IS CONSIDERED TO BE THE RICHEST PERSON IN THE WORLD.

WE MAKE A BEAUTIFUL HANDWOVEN CLOTH WITH GOLD AND SILVER THREADS.

THE POPULATION OF BRUNEI IS 300 THOUSAND. THEY SPEAK MALAY, CHINESE AND ENGLISH.

BRUNEI

BATIK IS A WAY OF PRINTING FABRIC HERE.

THE WORLD'S LARGEST CAVE CHAMBER IS IN SARAWAK, MALAYSIA. IT'S LARGE ENOUGH TO HOLD ABOUT 7,500 BUSES.

THE POPULATION OF MALAYSIA IS 19 MILLION, 900 THOUSAND, AND THEIR LANGUAGES ARE MALAY, CHINESE, TAMIL, AND ENGLISH.

BORNEO

ARE WE THERE, YET?

Z

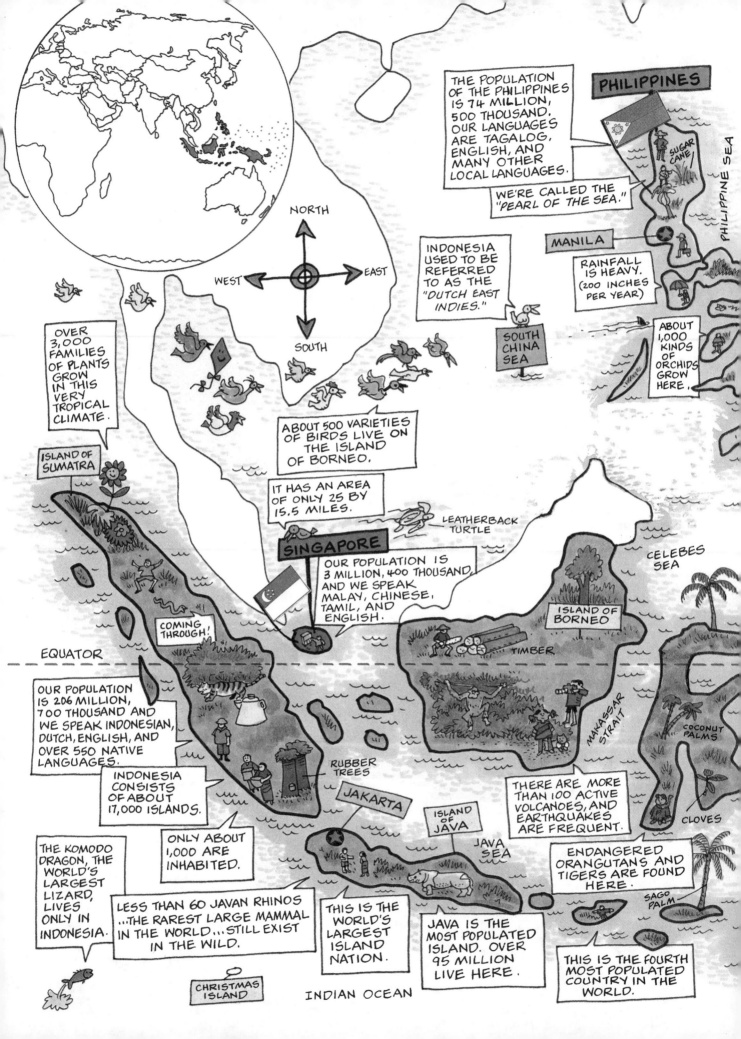

INDONESIA AND THE ISLAND NATIONS

The island nations of Southeastern Asia were an important source of spices for the Europeans, who fought to control the spice trade. The region was once known as the East Indies.

The islands receive lots of rain during the monsoon season. The climate in this heavily forested land is hot and sticky most of the year.

Find out all about Indonesia and the island nations, and where in the world they are. Then look for all of the following things, too.

- ☐ Airplane
- ☐ Coffeepot
- ☐ Kangaroo
- ☐ Kite
- ☐ Orangutan
- ☐ Photographer
- ☐ Rhinoceros
- ☐ Shark fins (4)
- ☐ Snakes (2)
- ☐ Tiger
- ☐ Turtle
- ☐ Volcanoes (2)

THE CLIMATE IS HOT AND HUMID.

OVER 80° IS THE AVERAGE TEMPERATURE.

THERE ARE OVER 7,000 ISLANDS IN THE PHILIPPINES, MOST OF THE PEOPLE LIVE ON THESE 11 ISLANDS.

BONIN ISLANDS

OF ABOUT 25,000 ISLANDS IN THE PACIFIC OCEAN, ONLY A FEW THOUSAND ARE INHABITED.

NORTHERN MARIANA ISLANDS

WAKE ISLAND

NORTH PACIFIC OCEAN

MARSHALL ISLANDS

SOME OF THE PACIFIC ISLANDS MAKE UP NINE INDEPENDENT COUNTRIES.

MANY OTHER ISLANDS ARE GOVERNED BY COUNTRIES SUCH AS THE U.S., GREAT BRITAIN, AND FRANCE.

PALAU

VOLCANIC ERUPTIONS ARE COMMON. THESE ISLANDS ARE ACTUALLY THE TOPS OF MOUNTAINS THAT ARE STILL FORMING.

FEDERATED STATES OF MICRONESIA

SOME OF THE ISLANDS ARE THE TIPS OF MOUNTAINS OR VOLCANOES, OTHERS ARE MADE UP OF CORAL.

I'M A PEARL OYSTER.

OUR POPULATION IS 4 MILLION, 400 THOUSAND. WE SPEAK ENGLISH, MELANESIAN, PLUS OVER 700 NATIVE LANGUAGES.

KIRIBATI

EQUATOR

MOLUCCA SEA

INDONESIA

PAPUA NEW GUINEA

MANY REMOTE TRIBES HAVE NO CONTACT WITH THE OUTSIDE WORLD.

HALF THE ISLAND BELONGS TO INDONESIA.

RAINFALL IS OVER 100 INCHES ANNUALLY.

BISMARCK SEA

MT. WILHELM (14,790 FT.)

TREE KANGAROO

BANDA SEA

INDONESIA'S MAIN EXPORTS ARE OIL, TIMBER, RUBBER AND COFFEE.

TUVALU

SOLOMON ISLANDS

MOST OF THE INTERIOR FOREST OF PAPUA NEW GUINEA IS ACCESSIBLE ONLY BY AIRCRAFT.

IT'S THE WORLD'S SECOND LARGEST ISLAND.

PORT MORESBY

VANUATU

FIJI

I CAN'T CARRY A TUNE... BUT, I'M A TUNA.

ARAFURA SEA

CORAL SEA ISLANDS

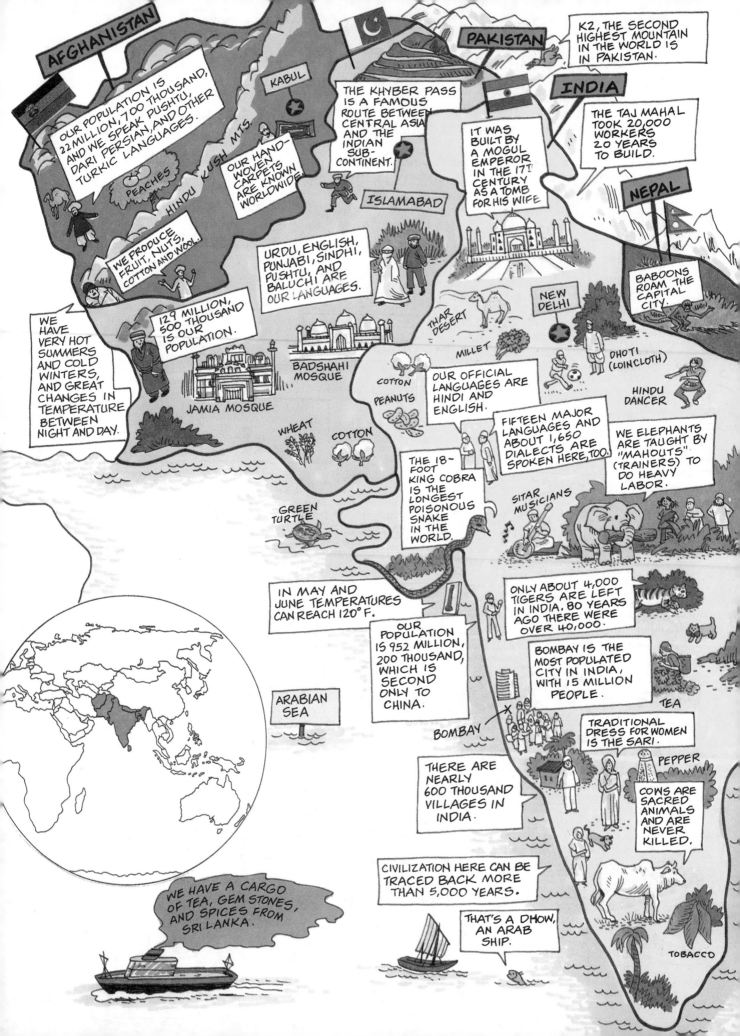

THE INDIAN SUBCONTINENT

Southern Asia is referred to as the Indian subcontinent. About 70% of the people in this heavily populated region depend of the land for their livelihood.

In 1947, when India became an independent country, it was divided along religious lines with the Moslems settling in Pakistan and the Hindus in India.

Find out all about the countries of the Indian subcontinent and where in the world they are. Then look for all of the following things, too.

- ☐ Camels (2)
- ☐ Carpets (2)
- ☐ Cow
- ☐ Bear
- ☐ Dancer
- ☐ Elephants (2)
- ☐ Fish (2)
- ☐ Monkeys (2)
- ☐ Musicians (2)
- ☐ Peanuts
- ☐ Pepper
- ☐ Snakes (2)
- ☐ Soccer ball
- ☐ Rhinoceros
- ☐ Turtle
- ☐ Umbrella

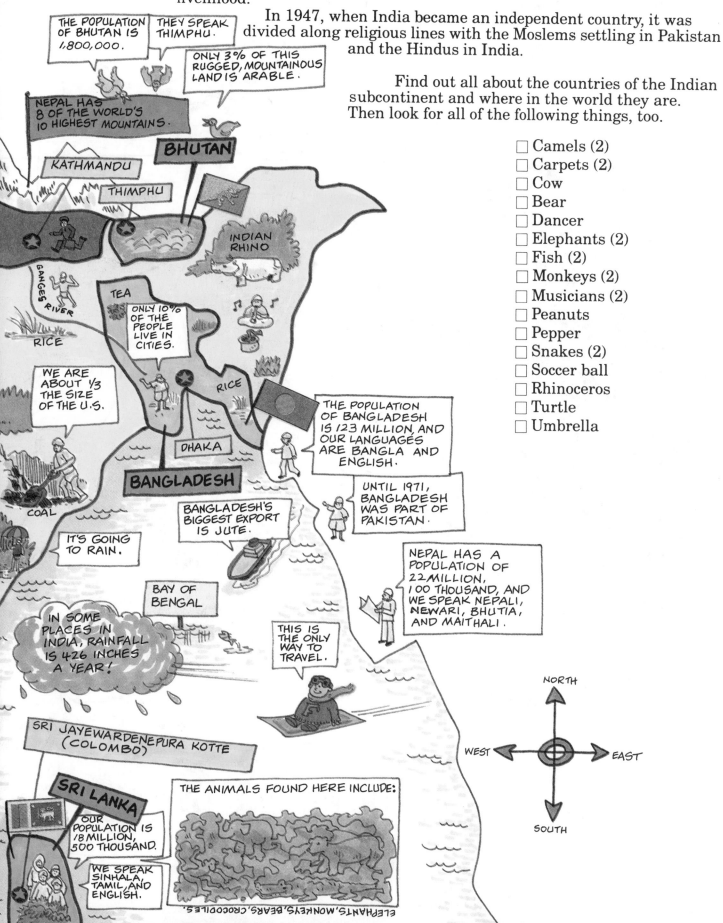

MT. EVEREST SITS ON THE BORDER BETWEEN NEPAL AND TIBET.

THE POPULATION OF BHUTAN IS 1,800,000.

THEY SPEAK THIMPHU.

ONLY 3% OF THIS RUGGED, MOUNTAINOUS LAND IS ARABLE.

NEPAL HAS 8 OF THE WORLD'S 10 HIGHEST MOUNTAINS.

BHUTAN

KATHMANDU

THIMPHU

INDIAN RHINO

GANGES RIVER

TEA

ONLY 10% OF THE PEOPLE LIVE IN CITIES.

RICE

WE ARE ABOUT 1/3 THE SIZE OF THE U.S.

RICE

DHAKA

BANGLADESH

THE POPULATION OF BANGLADESH IS 123 MILLION, AND OUR LANGUAGES ARE BANGLA AND ENGLISH.

UNTIL 1971, BANGLADESH WAS PART OF PAKISTAN.

COAL

BANGLADESH'S BIGGEST EXPORT IS JUTE.

IT'S GOING TO RAIN.

NEPAL HAS A POPULATION OF 22 MILLION, 100 THOUSAND, AND WE SPEAK NEPALI, NEWARI, BHUTIA, AND MAITHALI.

BAY OF BENGAL

IN SOME PLACES IN INDIA, RAINFALL IS 426 INCHES A YEAR!

THIS IS THE ONLY WAY TO TRAVEL.

SRI JAYEWARDENEPURA KOTTE (COLOMBO)

NORTH

WEST — EAST

SOUTH

SRI LANKA

OUR POPULATION IS 18 MILLION, 500 THOUSAND.

WE SPEAK SINHALA, TAMIL, AND ENGLISH.

THE ANIMALS FOUND HERE INCLUDE:

ELEPHANTS, MONKEYS, BEARS, CROCODILES.

THE MIDDLE EAST

One of the first places where civilization was recorded is in the area between the Tigris and Euphrates rivers. Towns and communities were thriving here 6,000 years ago. Today, the region produces about one-third of the world's petroleum.

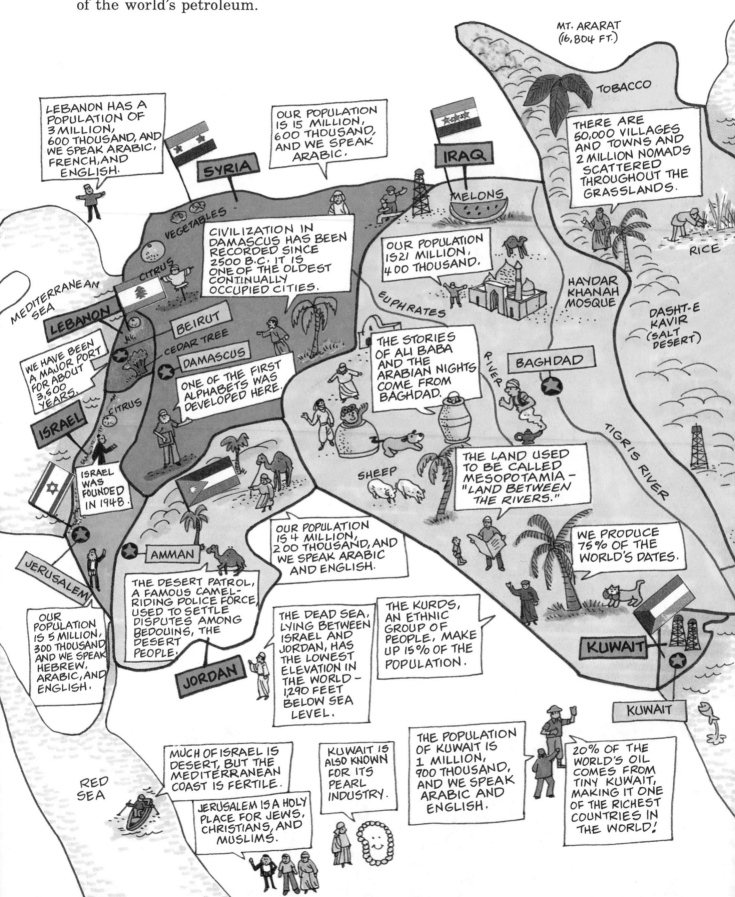

Find out all about the countries of the Middle East, and where in the world they are. Then look for all of the following things, too.

☐ Camels (5)
☐ Fish (2)
☐ Fish eggs
☐ Genie
☐ Melon
☐ Mosques (2)
☐ Pearl necklace
☐ Scarecrow
☐ Shovel
☐ Snake
☐ Tanker
☐ Teapot

CASPIAN SEA

TEA

CAVIAR IS PICKLED EGGS OF LARGE FISH.

CAVIAR

OUR POPULATION IS 66 MILLION.

TURQUOISE

OUR LANGUAGES ARE FARSI, KURDISH, AND ARABIC.

ELBURZ MTS.
TEHRAN

THE ROYAL MOSQUE

THIS IS THEIR TRADITIONAL DRESS.

COTTON

LAKE NAMAK

IRAN

NORTH

"PART-TIME" RIVERS KNOWN AS "WADIS" ARE DRY MOST OF THE YEAR.

PIGEON TOWERS

WEST

EAST

THEY FLOOD WHEN IT RAINS.

UNTIL 1935, THIS LAND WAS CALLED PERSIA.

GOATS

SILK

SOUTH

WE ARE STILL A POPULAR MEANS OF TRANSPORTATION.

IRAN IS FAMOUS FOR ITS PERSIAN RUGS.

SHEEP

CHEMICALS

CAN ANY OF THEM FLY?

IRAN IS VERY RICH IN PETROLEUM.

OUR CIVILIZATION IS NEARLY 6,000 YEARS OLD.

GAS

GAS

OIL TANKER

PERSIAN GULF

STRAIT OF HORMUZ

GULF OF OMAN

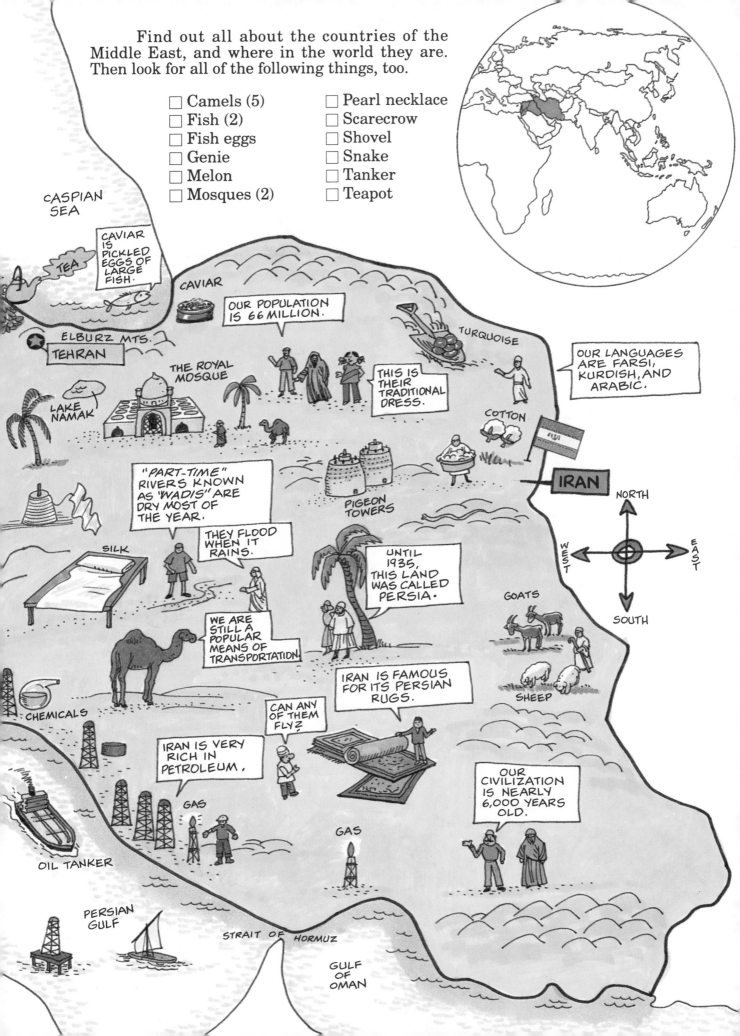

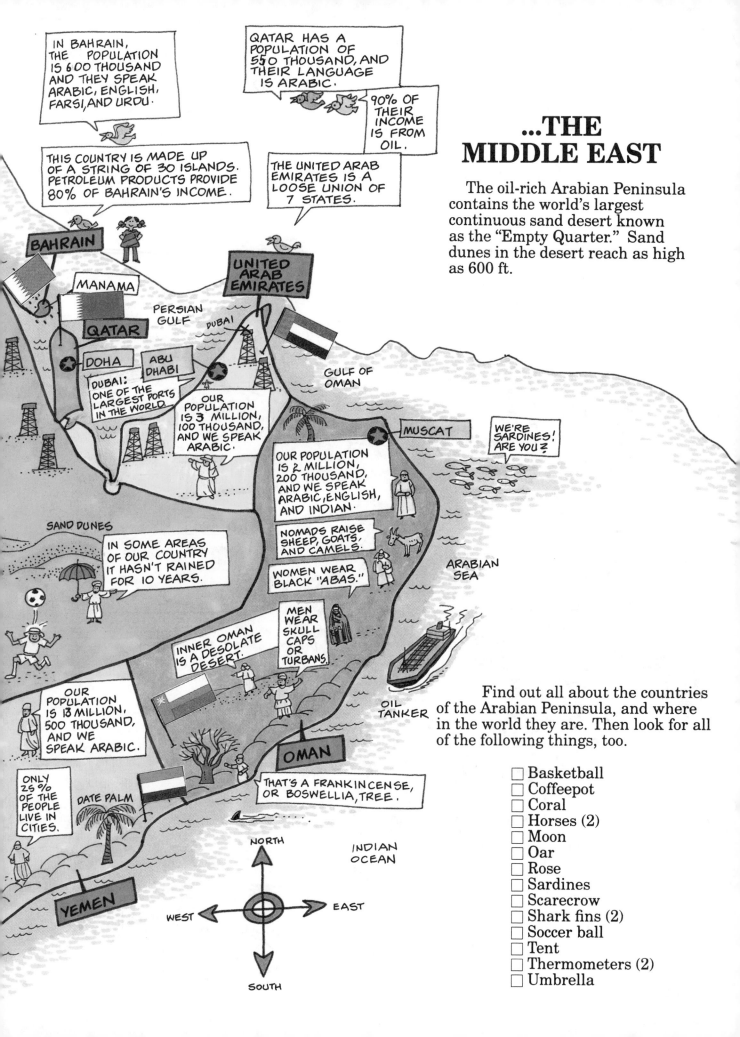

...THE MIDDLE EAST

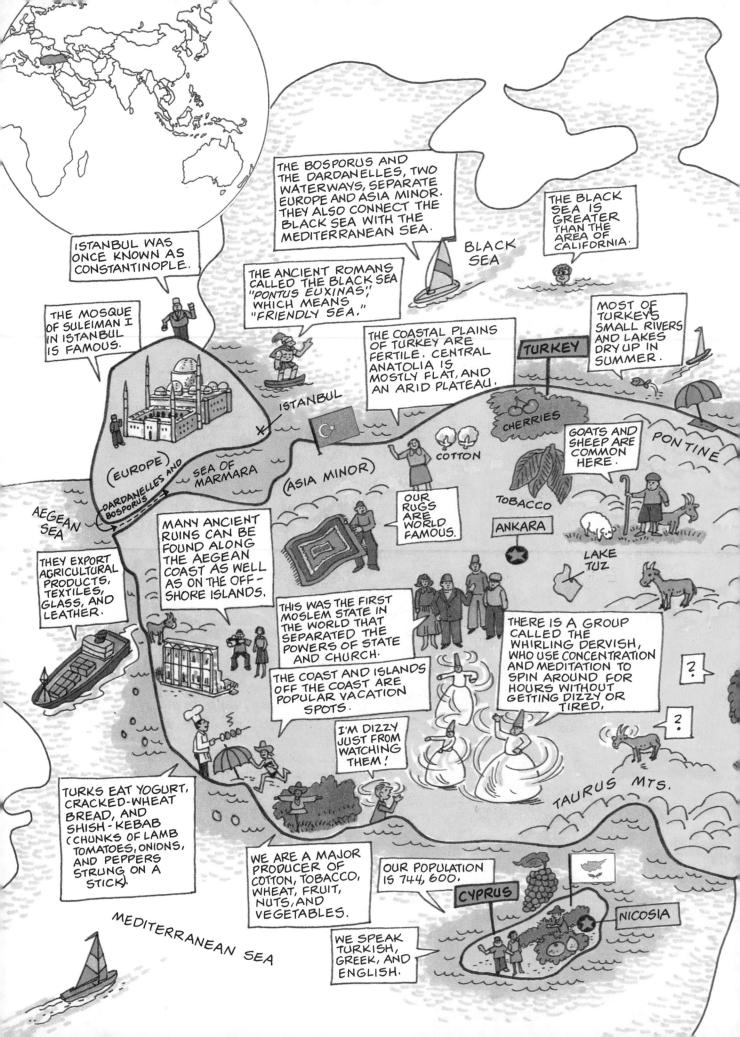

TURKEY AND CYPRUS

Three percent of Turkey lies in Europe. The rest is in Asia and is called Anatolia or Asia Minor. Istanbul is Turkey's largest city and the only city in the world that occupies land on two continents.

Find out all about Turkey and Cyprus, and where in the world they are. Then look for all of the following things, too.

☐ Apples
☐ Ball
☐ Bears (3)
☐ Book
☐ Cook
☐ Egg
☐ Fish
☐ Goats (5)
☐ Grapes

☐ Ibis
☐ Ladder
☐ Sailboats (3)
☐ Shepherd
☐ Tea bag
☐ Telescope
☐ Texan
☐ Tin man
☐ Umbrellas (2)

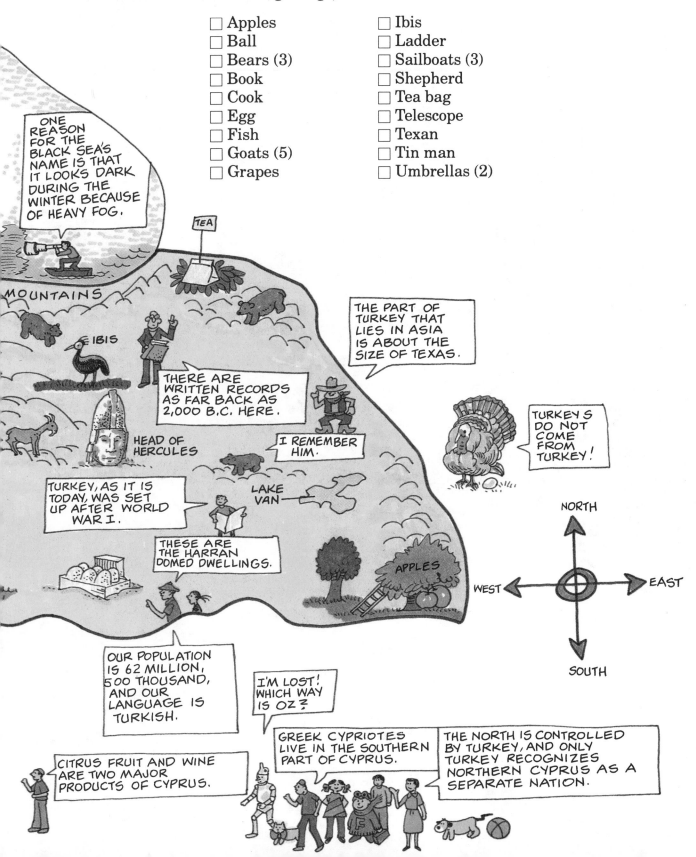

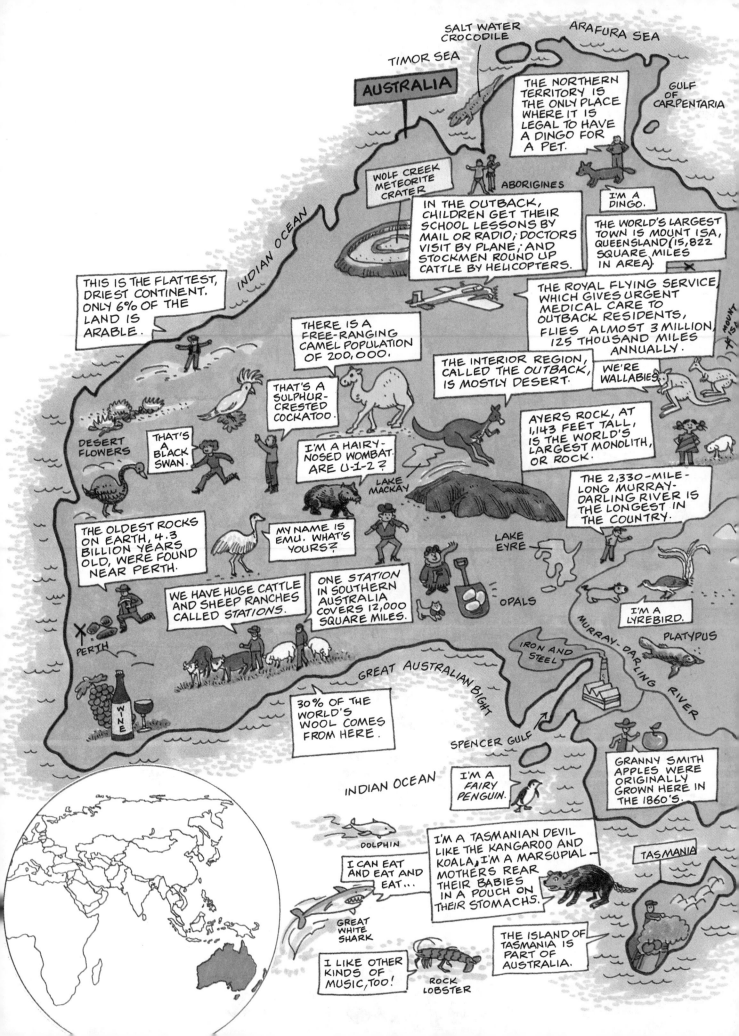

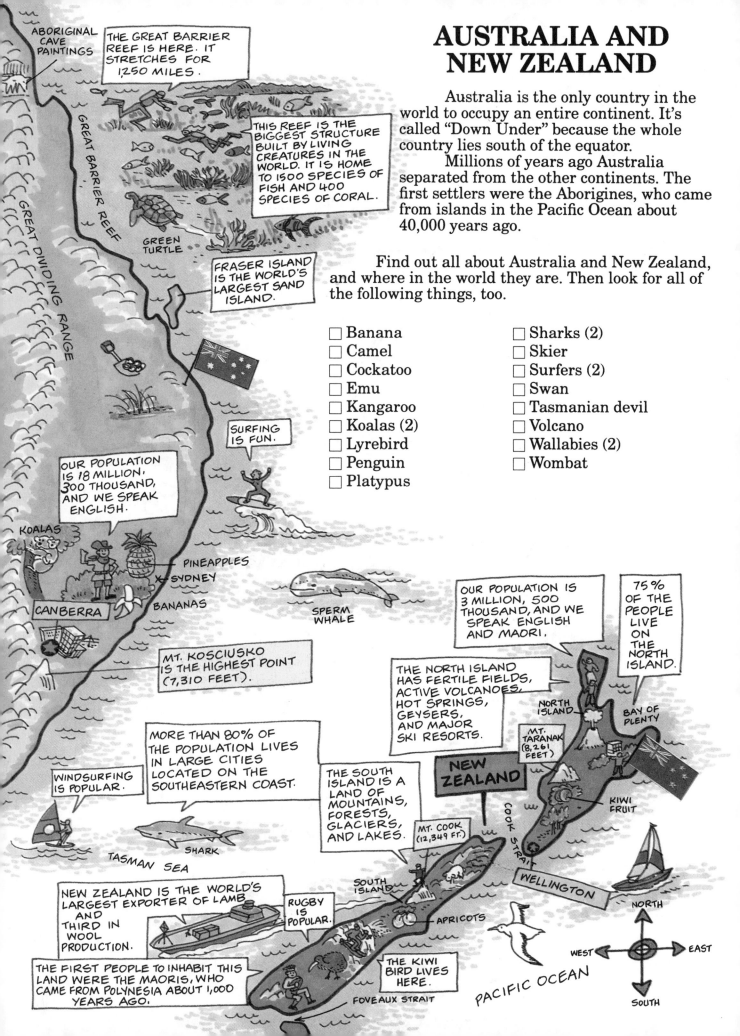

AUSTRALIA AND NEW ZEALAND

Australia is the only country in the world to occupy an entire continent. It's called "Down Under" because the whole country lies south of the equator.

Millions of years ago Australia separated from the other continents. The first settlers were the Aborigines, who came from islands in the Pacific Ocean about 40,000 years ago.

Find out all about Australia and New Zealand, and where in the world they are. Then look for all of the following things, too.

- ☐ Banana
- ☐ Camel
- ☐ Cockatoo
- ☐ Emu
- ☐ Kangaroo
- ☐ Koalas (2)
- ☐ Lyrebird
- ☐ Penguin
- ☐ Platypus
- ☐ Sharks (2)
- ☐ Skier
- ☐ Surfers (2)
- ☐ Swan
- ☐ Tasmanian devil
- ☐ Volcano
- ☐ Wallabies (2)
- ☐ Wombat

ABORIGINAL CAVE PAINTINGS

THE GREAT BARRIER REEF IS HERE. IT STRETCHES FOR 1,250 MILES.

GREAT BARRIER REEF

THIS REEF IS THE BIGGEST STRUCTURE BUILT BY LIVING CREATURES IN THE WORLD. IT IS HOME TO 1500 SPECIES OF FISH AND 400 SPECIES OF CORAL.

GREEN TURTLE

FRASER ISLAND IS THE WORLD'S LARGEST SAND ISLAND.

GREAT DIVIDING RANGE

SURFING IS FUN.

OUR POPULATION IS 18 MILLION, 300 THOUSAND, AND WE SPEAK ENGLISH.

KOALAS

CANBERRA

PINEAPPLES

SYDNEY

BANANAS

SPERM WHALE

OUR POPULATION IS 3 MILLION, 500 THOUSAND, AND WE SPEAK ENGLISH AND MAORI.

75% OF THE PEOPLE LIVE ON THE NORTH ISLAND.

THE NORTH ISLAND HAS FERTILE FIELDS, ACTIVE VOLCANOES, HOT SPRINGS, GEYSERS, AND MAJOR SKI RESORTS.

NORTH ISLAND

BAY OF PLENTY

MT. KOSCIUSKO IS THE HIGHEST POINT (7,310 FEET).

MT. TARANAK (8,261 FEET)

MORE THAN 80% OF THE POPULATION LIVES IN LARGE CITIES LOCATED ON THE SOUTHEASTERN COAST.

NEW ZEALAND

THE SOUTH ISLAND IS A LAND OF MOUNTAINS, FORESTS, GLACIERS, AND LAKES.

KIWI FRUIT

WINDSURFING IS POPULAR.

MT. COOK (12,349 FT.)

COOK STRAIT

SHARK

TASMAN SEA

SOUTH ISLAND

WELLINGTON

NEW ZEALAND IS THE WORLD'S LARGEST EXPORTER OF LAMB AND THIRD IN WOOL PRODUCTION.

RUGBY IS POPULAR.

APRICOTS

NORTH

THE FIRST PEOPLE TO INHABIT THIS LAND WERE THE MAORIS, WHO CAME FROM POLYNESIA ABOUT 1,000 YEARS AGO.

THE KIWI BIRD LIVES HERE.

WEST

EAST

FOVEAUX STRAIT

PACIFIC OCEAN

SOUTH

ANTARCTICA

Antarctica is the coldest place on earth, with temperatures as low as -125°F. Although it is larger than the United States, no one owns it. Only scientific research bases are there.

Find out all about Antarctica and where in the world it is. Then look for all of the following things, too.

☐ Baby penguin
☐ Dinosaur
☐ Elephant seals (3)
☐ Lost mitten
☐ Snowman
☐ Snowmobile
☐ Whales (3)

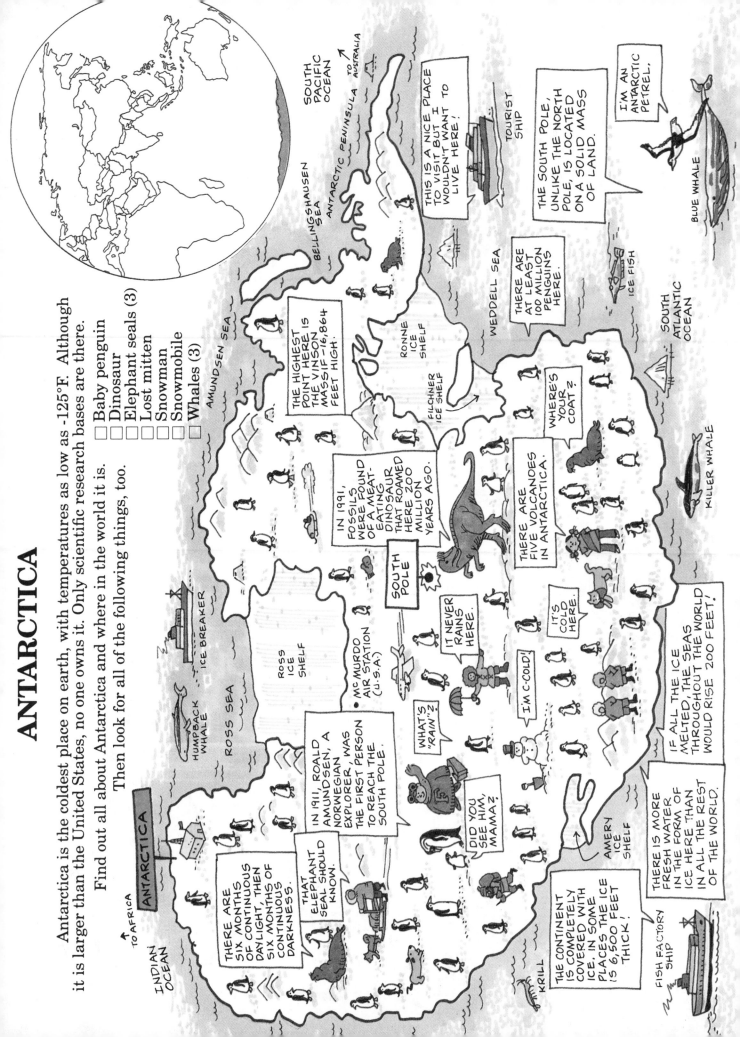

THIS IS A NICE PLACE TO VISIT BUT I WOULDN'T WANT TO LIVE HERE!

TOURIST SHIP

THE SOUTH POLE, UNLIKE THE NORTH POLE, IS LOCATED ON A SOLID MASS OF LAND.

I'M AN ANTARCTIC PETREL.

BLUE WHALE

THERE ARE AT LEAST 100 MILLION PENGUINS HERE.

ICE FISH

SOUTH ATLANTIC OCEAN

WHERE'S YOUR COAT?

KILLER WHALE

THE HIGHEST POINT HERE IS THE VINSON MASSIF —16,864 FEET HIGH.

SOUTH PACIFIC OCEAN

TO AUSTRALIA

ANTARCTIC PENINSULA

BELLINGSHAUSEN SEA

WEDDELL SEA

RONNE ICE SHELF

FILCHNER ICE SHELF

AMUNDSEN SEA

IN 1991, FOSSILS WERE FOUND OF A MEAT-EATING DINOSAUR THAT ROAMED HERE 200 MILLION YEARS AGO.

THERE ARE FIVE VOLCANOES IN ANTARCTICA.

SOUTH POLE

IT NEVER RAINS HERE.

IT'S COLD HERE.

I'M C-COLD!

ICE BREAKER

ROSS SEA

ROSS ICE SHELF

HUMPBACK WHALE

McMURDO AIR STATION (U.S.A.)

WHAT'S "RAIN"?

IN 1911, ROALD AMUNDSEN, A NORWEGIAN EXPLORER, WAS THE FIRST PERSON TO REACH THE SOUTH POLE.

DID YOU SEE HIM, MAMA?

THAT ELEPHANT SEAL SHOULD KNOW.

THERE ARE SIX MONTHS OF CONTINUOUS DAYLIGHT, THEN SIX MONTHS OF CONTINUOUS DARKNESS.

TO AFRICA

ANTARCTICA

INDIAN OCEAN

AMERY ICE SHELF

THE CONTINENT IS COMPLETELY COVERED WITH ICE. IN SOME PLACES THE ICE IS 6,500 FEET THICK!

THERE IS MORE FRESH WATER IN THE FORM OF ICE HERE THAN IN ALL THE REST OF THE WORLD.

IF ALL THE ICE MELTED, THE SEAS THROUGHOUT THE WORLD WOULD RISE 200 FEET!

KRILL

FISH FACTORY SHIP

EUROPE

II

Search and find lots of interesting facts about:

- **The British Isles**

- **Scandinavia**

- **The Iberian Peninsula**

- **The Low Countries and Luxembourg**

- **France**

- **The Italian Peninsula**

- **Central Europe**

- **Eastern Europe**

- **Eastern Europe and the Baltic States**

- **The Balkan States**

- **Greece**

EUROPE

The seat of western civilization, Europe has had a strong influence on the world through trade, exploration, and industry.

The continent stretches from the icy Arctic Circle in the north to the warm Mediterranean Sea in the south. The land, with its great fertile plains and tall mountains, is as varied as its people and the countries it contains.

Find out all about the countries of Europe, and where in the world they are. Then look for all of the following things, too.

☐ Cyclist
☐ Eiffel Tower
☐ Fish (3)
☐ Grapes
☐ Puffin
☐ Sailboat
☐ Volcano
☐ Windmill
☐ Wooden shoe

FINLAND

RUSSIA

LAKE LADOGA

ESTONIA

LATVIA

LITHUANIA

BELARUS

FLAX

SUGAR BEETS

UKRAINE

MOLDOVA

WHEAT

DNIEPER RV.

DON RIVER

VOLGA RIVER

HIGHEST POINT IN EUROPE IS MT. ELBRUS IN THE CAUCASUS RANGE IN RUSSIA.

CAUCASUS

THE VOLGA (RUNNING FOR 2,290 MILES) IS THE LONGEST RIVER IN EUROPE.

CASPIAN SEA

ROMANIA

TRANSYLVANIAN ALPS

THE DANUBE RIVER FLOWS THROUGH 7 EUROPEAN COUNTRIES.

EUROPE IS CONSIDERED THE BIRTHPLACE OF WESTERN CIVILIZATION.

THE BLACK SEA

NORTH
EAST
WEST
SOUTH

BULGARIA

TURKEY

EUROPE OCCUPIES ONLY 6.6% OF THE WORLD'S LAND AREA. IT IS THE 2ND SMALLEST CONTINENT, BUT IS HOME TO MORE PEOPLE THAN NORTH AND SOUTH AMERICA COMBINED.

EUROPE HAS AN AREA OF 3 MILLION, 800 THOUSAND SQUARE MILES.

ITS POPULATION IS 788 MILLION.

THE LARGEST LAKE IN EUROPE IS LADOGA, RUSSIA. (7,000 SQ. MILES)

The British Isles

The British Isles are made up of two countries, Ireland and the United Kingdom, also known as Great Britain. The United Kingdom consists of England, Scotland, Wales, and Northern Ireland. In the 18th century Great Britain was the world's leading industrial and trading nation. Its worldwide empire included Canada, India, Australia, New Zealand, and parts of Africa. Today, 50 former colonies are part of the British Commonwealth of Nations.

Find out all about Ireland and the United Kingdom, and where in the world they are. Then look for all of the following things, too.

- [ ] Bagpipe
- [ ] "Big Ben"
- [ ] Bus
- [ ] Clock
- [ ] Cricket
- [ ] Crystal
- [ ] Deer
- [ ] Ferry
- [ ] Four-leaf clover
- [ ] Golf
- [ ] Knight in armor
- [ ] Lobster
- [ ] "Nessie"
- [ ] Sheep (3)
- [ ] Soccer ball
- [ ] Stonehenge
- [ ] Student
- [ ] Tennis racket

BAA.

SHETLAND ISLANDS

HOME OF THE SHETLAND PONY

SEALS

ORKNEY ISLANDS

UNITED KINGDOM OF GREAT BRITAIN

NORTH SEA

EDINBURGH

THERE ARE HUGE OIL AND NATURAL GAS RESERVES IN THE NORTH SEA.

BALMORAL CASTLE

SCOTLAND

THAT'S THE MYTHICAL LOCH (LAKE) NESS MONSTER

BEN NEVIS 4,406 FEET-HIGHEST MOUNTAIN.

HELLO, I'M "NESSIE."

GLASGOW IS BRITAIN'S GREATEST INDUSTRIAL CENTER.

HOME OF THE BAGPIPE

RED DEER

HOME OF HARRIS TWEED

OUTER HEBRIDES

INNER HEBRIDES

NORTH UIST

SOUTH UIST

BAA!

SHIP BUILDING

WHEN IRELAND BECAME INDEPENDENT FROM BRITAIN IN 1921, NORTHERN IRELAND CHOSE TO REMAIN A PART OF THE UNITED KINGDOM.

NORTHERN IRELAND

BELFAST

TEXTILES-LACE

ATLANTIC OCEAN

OUR POPULATION IS 3 MILLION, 560 THOUSAND, AND WE SPEAK IRISH (GAELIC) AND ENGLISH.

DONEGAL BAY

POTATOES

THE IRISH LEGEND OF THE BLARNEY STONE SAYS THAT ANYONE WHO KISSES IT RECEIVES THE GIFT OF GAB.

IRELAND

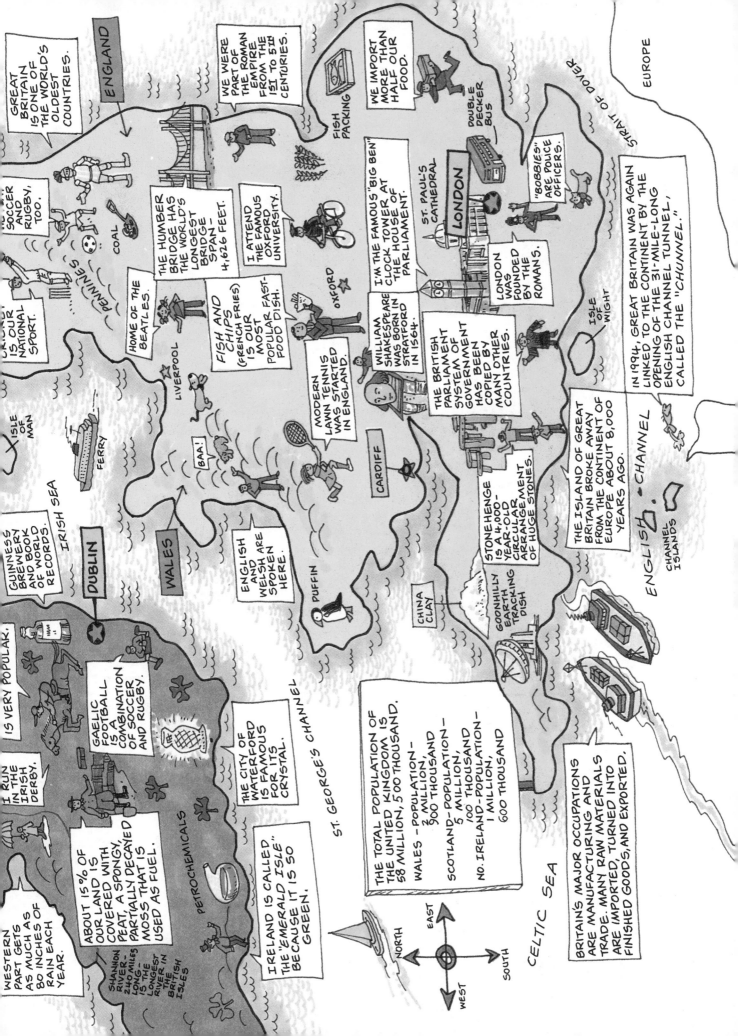

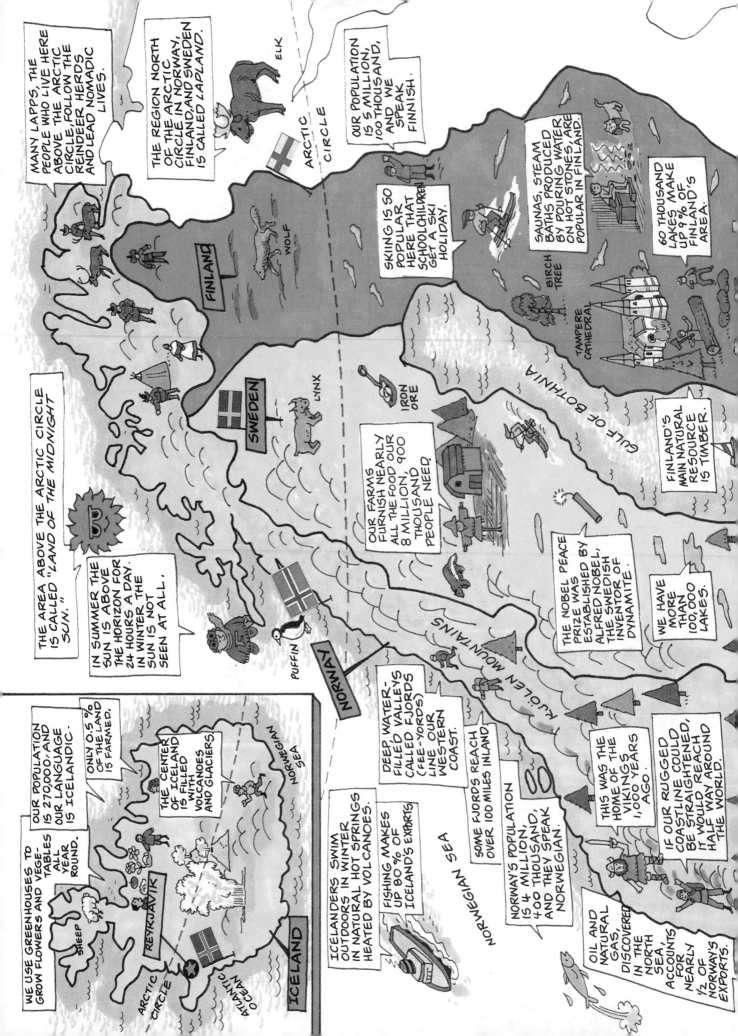

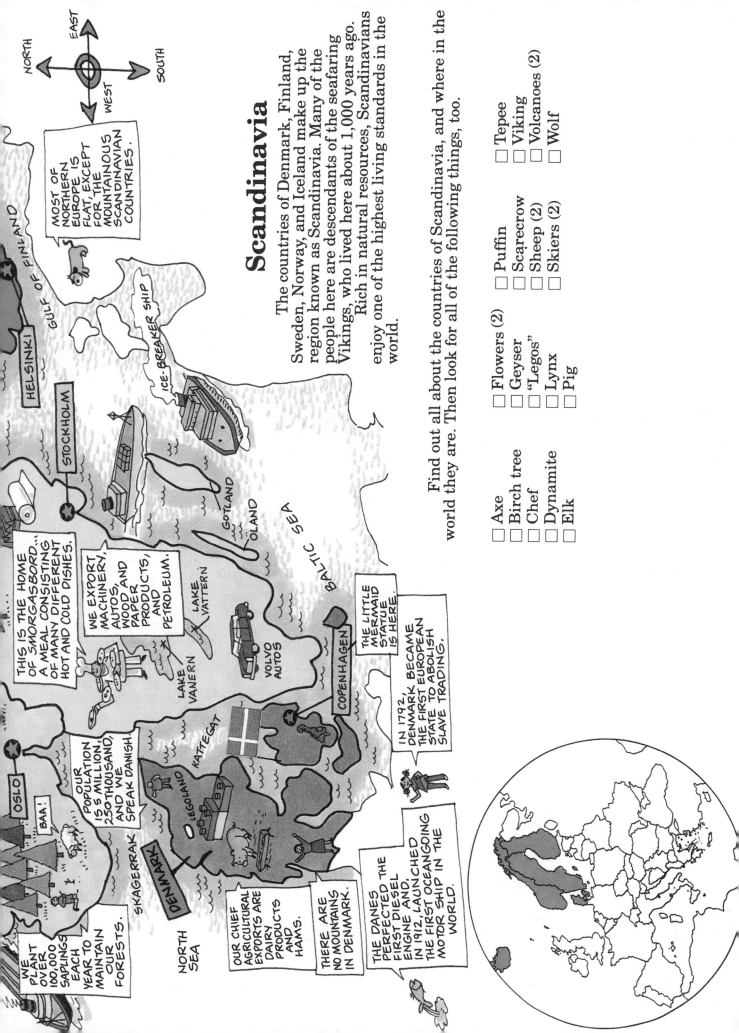

Scandinavia

The countries of Denmark, Finland, Sweden, Norway, and Iceland make up the region known as Scandinavia. Many of the people here are descendants of the seafaring Vikings, who lived here about 1,000 years ago.

Rich in natural resources, Scandinavians enjoy one of the highest living standards in the world.

Find out all about the countries of Scandinavia, and where in the world they are. Then look for all of the following things, too.

- ☐ Axe
- ☐ Birch tree
- ☐ Chef
- ☐ Dynamite
- ☐ Elk

- ☐ Flowers (2)
- ☐ Geyser
- ☐ "Legos"
- ☐ Lynx
- ☐ Pig

- ☐ Puffin
- ☐ Scarecrow
- ☐ Sheep (2)
- ☐ Skiers (2)

- ☐ Tepee
- ☐ Viking
- ☐ Volcanoes (2)
- ☐ Wolf

NORTH EAST SOUTH WEST

MOST OF NORTHERN EUROPE IS FLAT, EXCEPT FOR THE MOUNTAINOUS SCANDINAVIAN COUNTRIES.

GULF OF FINLAND

HELSINKI

ICE-BREAKER SHIP

STOCKHOLM

GOTLAND

ÖLAND

BALTIC SEA

THIS IS THE HOME OF SMORGASBORD... A MEAL CONSISTING OF MANY DIFFERENT HOT AND COLD DISHES.

WE EXPORT MACHINERY, AUTOS, WOOD AND PAPER PRODUCTS, AND PETROLEUM.

LAKE VÄTTERN

LAKE VÄNERN

VOLVO AUTOS

COPENHAGEN

THE LITTLE MERMAID STATUE IS HERE.

IN 1792, DENMARK BECAME THE FIRST EUROPEAN STATE TO ABOLISH SLAVE TRADING.

OSLO

BAA!

OUR POPULATION IS 5 MILLION, 250 THOUSAND, AND WE SPEAK DANISH.

KATTEGAT

LEGOLAND

SKAGERRAK

DENMARK

NORTH SEA

OUR CHIEF AGRICULTURAL EXPORTS ARE DAIRY PRODUCTS AND HAMS.

THERE ARE NO MOUNTAINS IN DENMARK.

THE DANES PERFECTED THE FIRST DIESEL ENGINE AND, IN 1912, LAUNCHED THE FIRST OCEANGOING MOTOR SHIP IN THE WORLD.

WE PLANT OVER 100,000 SAPLINGS EACH YEAR TO MAINTAIN OUR FORESTS.

The Iberian Peninsula

Spain and Portugal share a piece of land called the Iberian Peninsula. Both countries have a long seafaring history. Their explorers and settlers came to rule empires in Africa, Asia, and North and South America.

Today, fishing, farming, and tourism are major industries in both countries. More than 60 million tourists each year visit the historical cities and sun-drenched beaches of Spain and Portugal.

Find out all about Spain and Portugal, and where in the world they are. Then look for all of the following things, too.

- ☐ Anchovies
- ☐ Bottles (5)
- ☐ Brown bear
- ☐ Bulls (3)
- ☐ Car
- ☐ Cheese
- ☐ Cork
- ☐ Guitar
- ☐ Ibex
- ☐ Olive tree
- ☐ Skier
- ☐ Sunflowers (4)
- ☐ Umbrellas (3)
- ☐ Windmill
- ☐ Windsurfers (3)

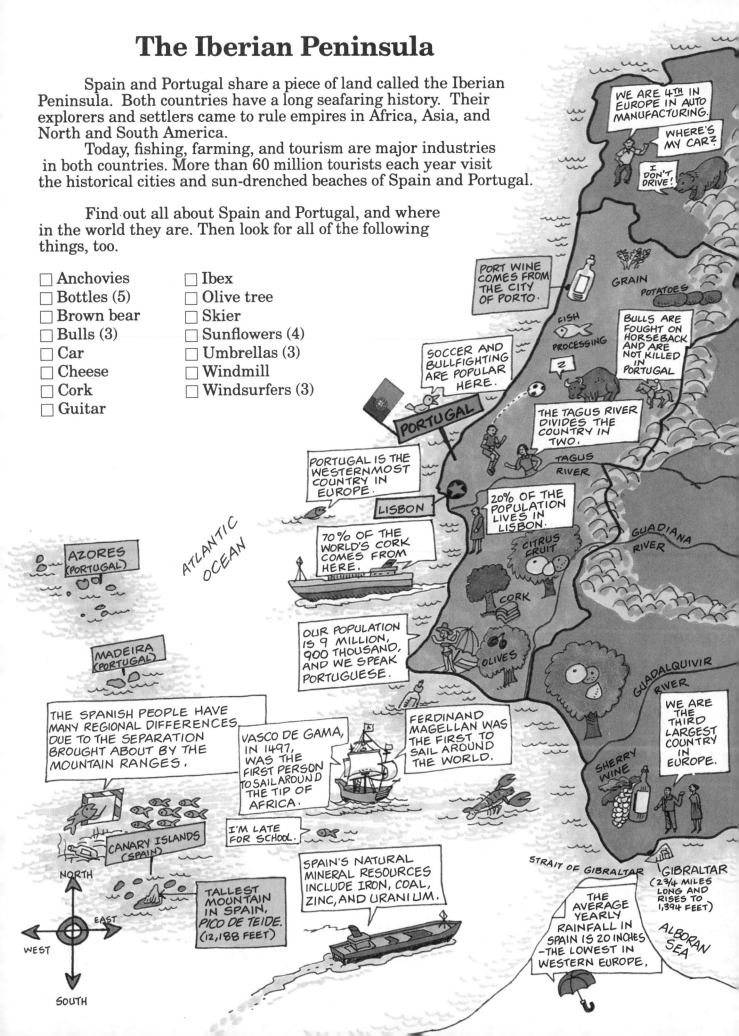

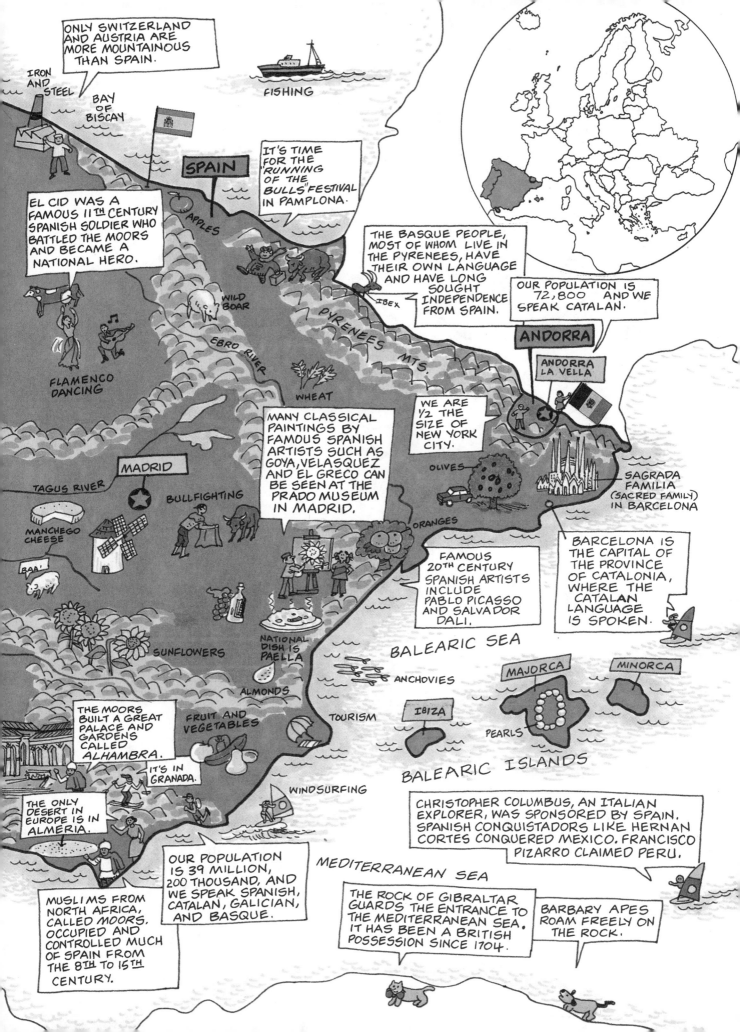

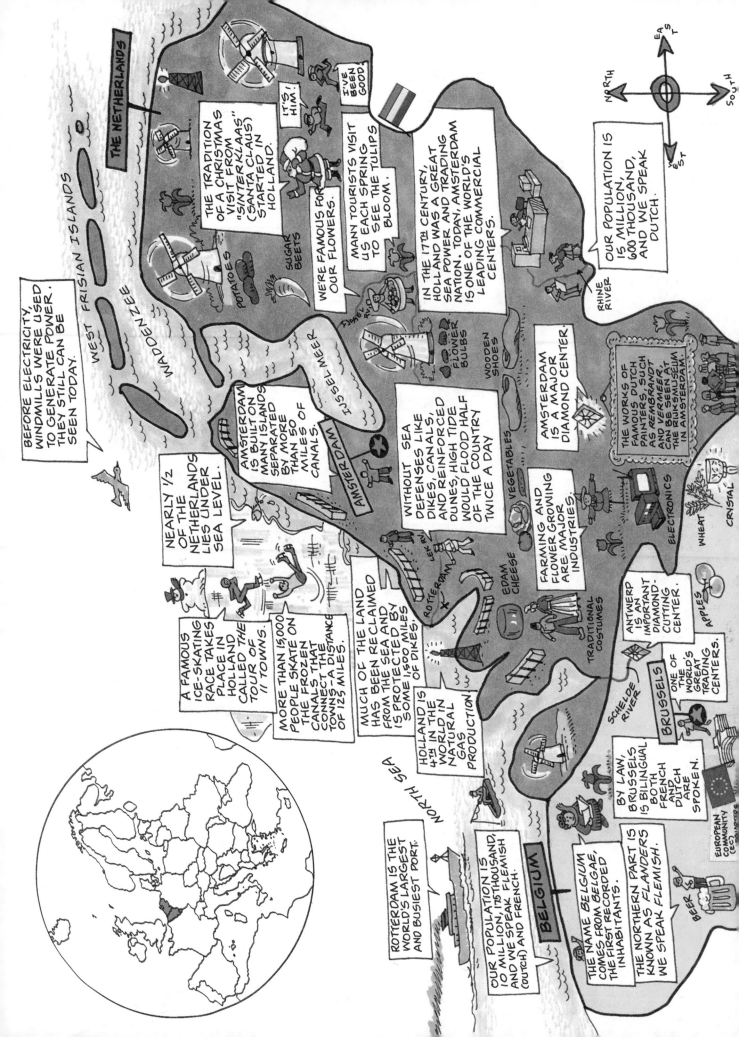

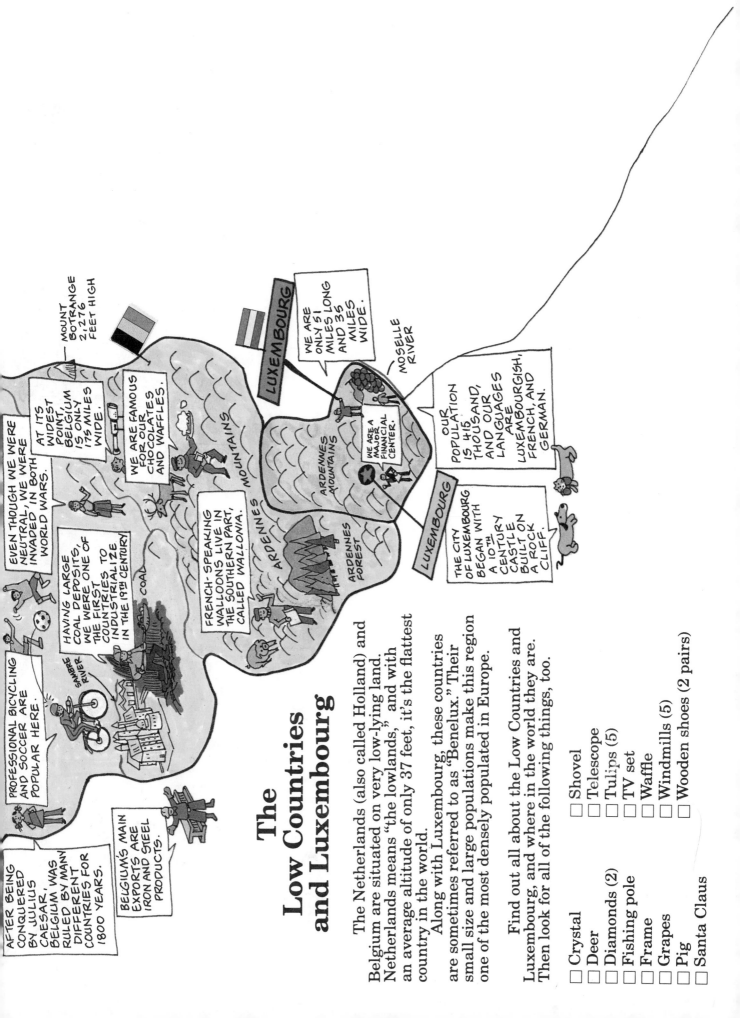

The Low Countries and Luxembourg

The Netherlands (also called Holland) and Belgium are situated on very low-lying land. Netherlands means "the lowlands," and with an average altitude of only 37 feet, it's the flattest country in the world.

Along with Luxembourg, these countries are sometimes referred to as "Benelux." Their small size and large populations make this region one of the most densely populated in Europe.

Find out all about the Low Countries and Luxembourg, and where in the world they are. Then look for all of the following things, too.

- ☐ Crystal
- ☐ Deer
- ☐ Diamonds (2)
- ☐ Fishing pole
- ☐ Frame
- ☐ Grapes
- ☐ Pig
- ☐ Santa Claus
- ☐ Shovel
- ☐ Telescope
- ☐ Tulips (5)
- ☐ TV set
- ☐ Waffle
- ☐ Windmills (5)
- ☐ Wooden shoes (2 pairs)

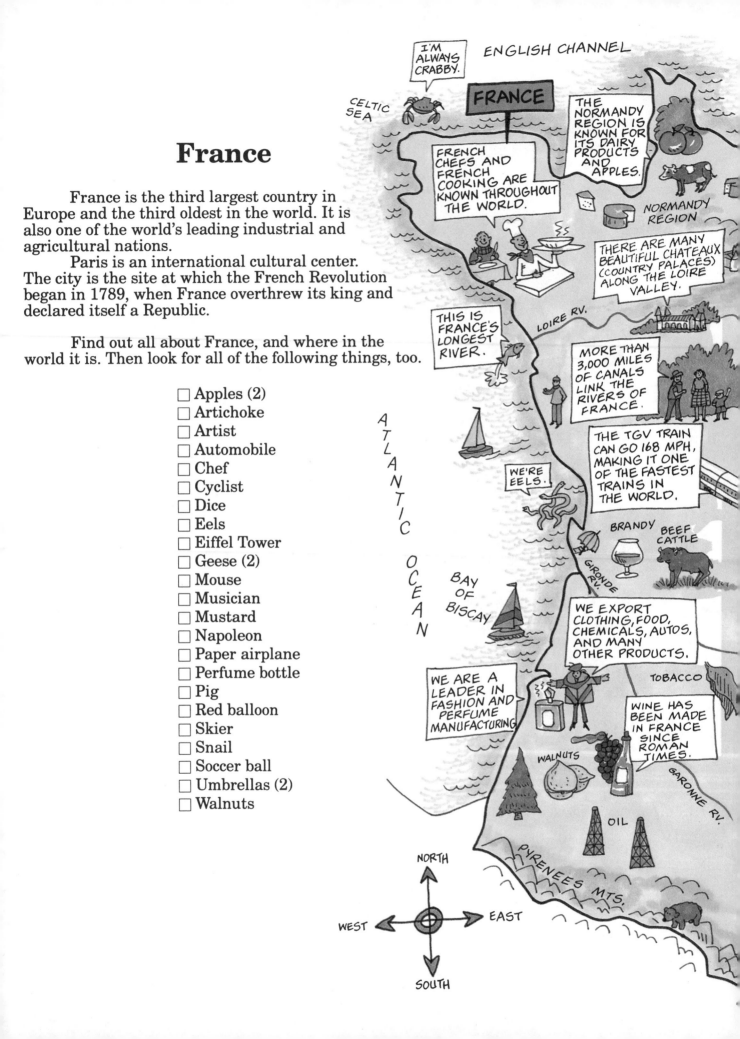

France

France is the third largest country in Europe and the third oldest in the world. It is also one of the world's leading industrial and agricultural nations.

Paris is an international cultural center. The city is the site at which the French Revolution began in 1789, when France overthrew its king and declared itself a Republic.

Find out all about France, and where in the world it is. Then look for all of the following things, too.

☐ Apples (2)
☐ Artichoke
☐ Artist
☐ Automobile
☐ Chef
☐ Cyclist
☐ Dice
☐ Eels
☐ Eiffel Tower
☐ Geese (2)
☐ Mouse
☐ Musician
☐ Mustard
☐ Napoleon
☐ Paper airplane
☐ Perfume bottle
☐ Pig
☐ Red balloon
☐ Skier
☐ Snail
☐ Soccer ball
☐ Umbrellas (2)
☐ Walnuts

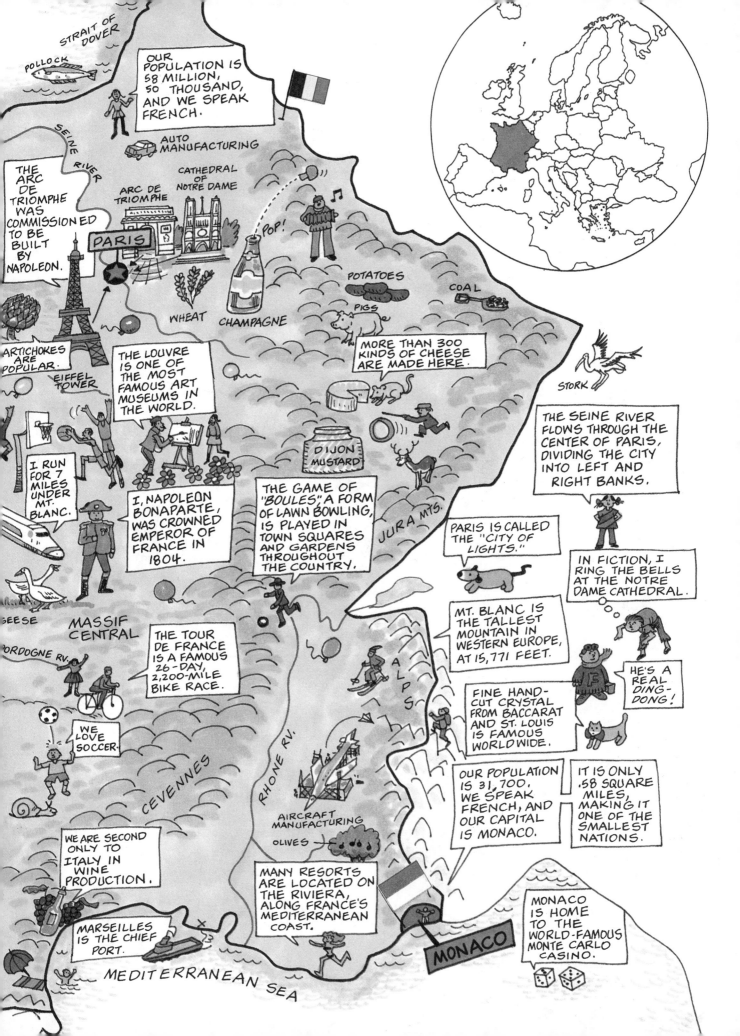

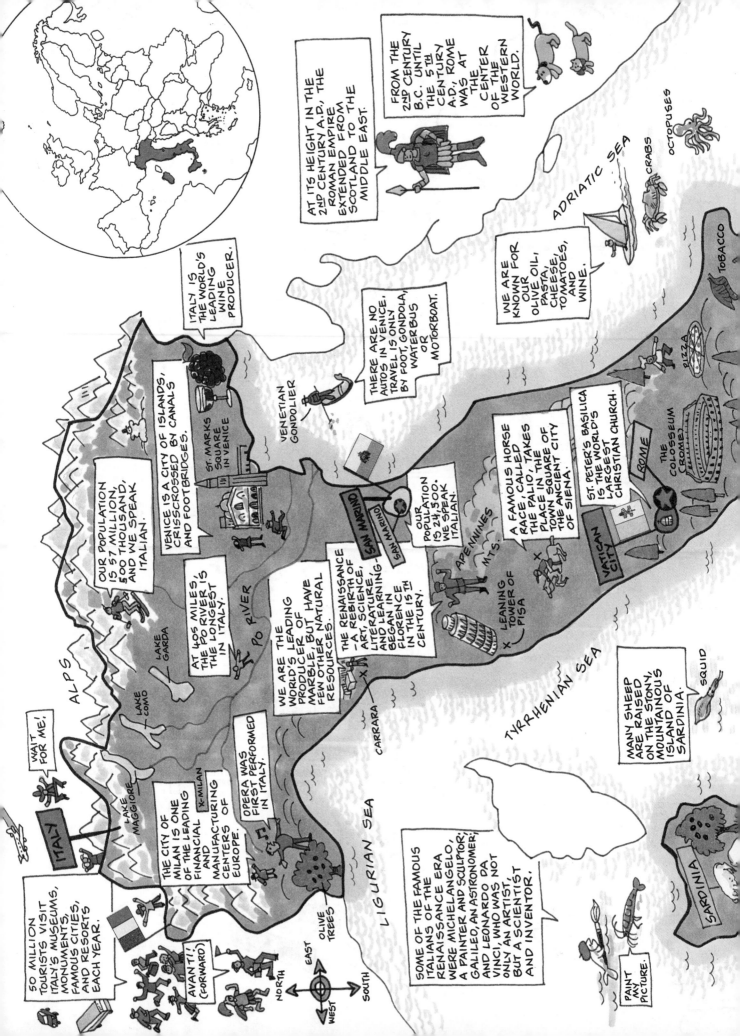

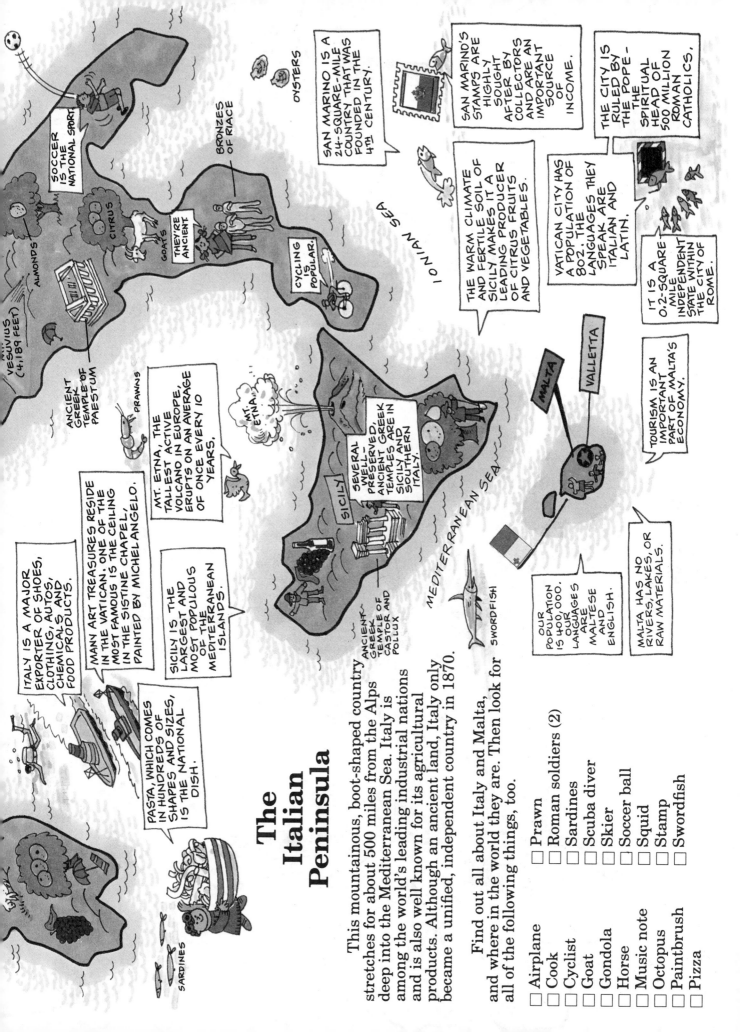

The Italian Peninsula

This mountainous, boot-shaped country stretches for about 500 miles from the Alps deep into the Mediterranean Sea. Italy is among the world's leading industrial nations and is also well known for its agricultural products. Although an ancient land, Italy only became a unified, independent country in 1870.

Find out all about Italy and Malta, and where in the world they are. Then look for all of the following things, too.

- ☐ Airplane
- ☐ Cook
- ☐ Cyclist
- ☐ Goat
- ☐ Gondola
- ☐ Horse
- ☐ Music note
- ☐ Octopus
- ☐ Paintbrush
- ☐ Pizza
- ☐ Prawn
- ☐ Roman soldiers (2)
- ☐ Sardines
- ☐ Scuba diver
- ☐ Skier
- ☐ Soccer ball
- ☐ Squid
- ☐ Stamp
- ☐ Swordfish

SOCCER IS THE NATIONAL SPORT.

OYSTERS

SAN MARINO IS A 24-SQUARE-MILE COUNTRY THAT WAS FOUNDED IN THE 4TH CENTURY.

SAN MARINO'S STAMPS ARE HIGHLY SOUGHT AFTER BY COLLECTORS AND ARE AN IMPORTANT SOURCE OF INCOME.

THE CITY IS RULED BY THE POPE— THE SPIRITUAL HEAD OF 500 MILLION ROMAN CATHOLICS.

BRONZES OF RIACE

ALMONDS

CITRUS

GOATS

THEY'RE ANCIENT

VESUVIUS (4,189 FEET)

ANCIENT GREEK TEMPLE OF PAESTUM

CYCLING IS POPULAR.

IONIAN SEA

THE WARM CLIMATE AND FERTILE SOIL OF SICILY MAKES IT A LEADING PRODUCER OF CITRUS FRUITS AND VEGETABLES.

VATICAN CITY HAS A POPULATION OF 802. THE LANGUAGES THEY SPEAK ARE ITALIAN AND LATIN.

IT IS A 0.2-SQUARE MILE INDEPENDENT STATE WITHIN THE CITY OF ROME.

VALLETTA

MALTA

PRAWNS

MT. ETNA, THE TALLEST ACTIVE VOLCANO IN EUROPE, ERUPTS ON AN AVERAGE OF ONCE EVERY 10 YEARS.

MT. ETNA

SICILY

SEVERAL WELL-PRESERVED, ANCIENT GREEK TEMPLES ARE IN SICILY AND SOUTHERN ITALY.

ITALY IS A MAJOR EXPORTER OF SHOES, CLOTHING, AUTOS, CHEMICALS AND FOOD PRODUCTS.

MANY ART TREASURES RESIDE IN THE VATICAN. ONE OF THE MOST FAMOUS IS THE CEILING IN THE SISTINE CHAPEL, PAINTED BY MICHELANGELO.

SICILY IS THE LARGEST AND MOST POPULOUS OF THE MEDITERRANEAN ISLANDS.

PASTA, WHICH COMES IN HUNDREDS OF SHAPES AND SIZES, IS THE NATIONAL DISH.

ANCIENT GREEK TEMPLE OF CASTOR AND POLLUX

MEDITERRANEAN SEA

SWORDFISH

TOURISM IS AN IMPORTANT PART OF MALTA'S ECONOMY.

OUR POPULATION IS 400,000. OUR LANGUAGES ARE MALTESE AND ENGLISH.

MALTA HAS NO RIVERS, LAKES, OR RAW MATERIALS.

SARDINES

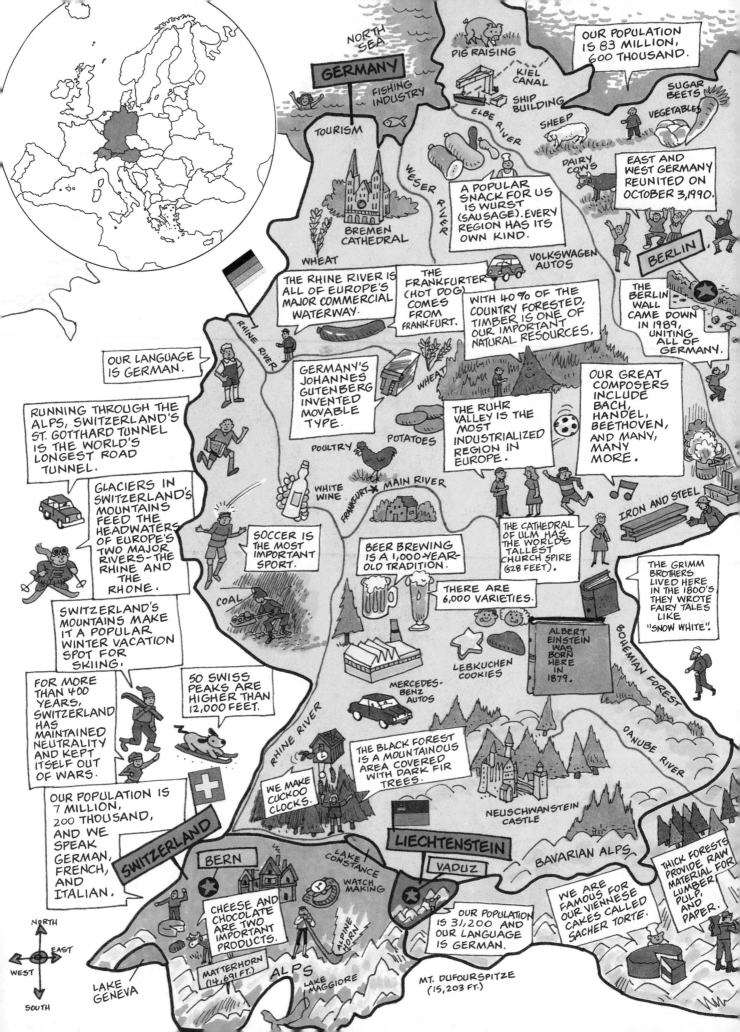

Central Europe

From north to south, this region's landscape changes from marshy plains to snowcapped mountains. It is crossed by two of Europe's longest rivers—the Rhine and the Danube—and by the famous Alps, the longest and highest mountain range in western Europe.

Find out all about the countries of central Europe, and where in the world they are. Then look for all of the following things, too.

- ☐ Automobiles (3)
- ☐ Axe
- ☐ Berlin Wall
- ☐ Books (3)
- ☐ Cake
- ☐ Chicken
- ☐ Coal miner
- ☐ Cookies
- ☐ Cows (2)
- ☐ Cuckoo clock
- ☐ Dogs (2)
- ☐ Heron
- ☐ Horse
- ☐ Hot dog
- ☐ Pigs (2)
- ☐ Soccer ball
- ☐ Telescope
- ☐ Tuba
- ☐ Watch

BALTIC SEA

TEXTILES

HISTORICALLY, THE LAND OF GERMANY HAS BEEN MORE DIVIDED THAN UNITED, CONSISTING OF SMALL INDEPENDENT STATES.

AFTER GERMANY WAS DEFEATED IN WORLD WAR II THE COUNTRY WAS DIVIDED INTO EAST AND WEST GERMANY. BERLIN WAS DIVIDED BY A CONCRETE WALL IN 1961. TODAY GERMANY IS UNITED.

GERMANY IS ONE OF THE WORLD'S MOST INDUSTRIALIZED COUNTRIES. WE EXPORT AUTOS, MACHINES, CHEMICALS, ELECTRONICS, AND IRON AND STEEL PRODUCTS.

AUSTRIA

VIENNA OPERA HOUSE

WE ARE FAMOUS FOR OUR TRADITIONAL MUSIC.

VIENNA

OUR POPULATION IS 8 MILLION, 25 THOUSAND, AND WE SPEAK GERMAN.

THE WORLD FAMOUS LIPIZZANER HORSES COME FROM AUSTRIA.

I'M A GREAT WHITE HERON FROM AUSTRIA.

WOLFGANG AMADEUS MOZART WAS BORN IN SALZBURG, AUSTRIA IN 1756.

ABOUT 3/4 OF THE COUNTRY IS COVERED BY THE ALPS.

THE HIGHEST PEAK IN AUSTRIA IS THE GROSSGLOCKNER (GREAT BELL), AT 12,461 FEET.

LIECHTENSTEIN WAS FOUNDED IN 1719 AND IS ABOUT THE SIZE OF WASHINGTON, D.C.

THE RHINE VALLEY COVERS 1/3 OF THE COUNTRY AND THE ALPS COVER THE REST.

LIECHTENSTEIN IS IN AN ECONOMIC UNION WITH SWITZERLAND. FOR MORE THAN 100 YEARS, THE COUNTRY HAS HAD NO ARMY, ONLY LOCAL POLICE.

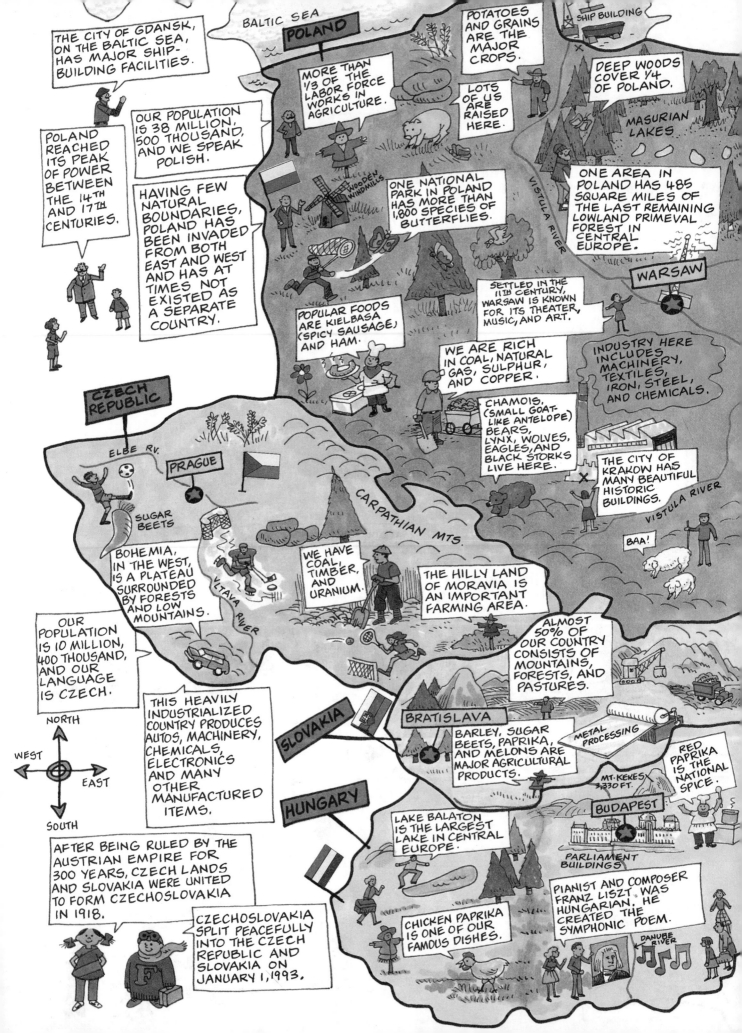

BALTIC SEA

POLAND

SHIP BUILDING

THE CITY OF GDANSK, ON THE BALTIC SEA, HAS MAJOR SHIP-BUILDING FACILITIES.

POTATOES AND GRAINS ARE THE MAJOR CROPS.

MORE THAN 1/3 OF THE LABOR FORCE WORKS IN AGRICULTURE.

LOTS OF US ARE RAISED HERE.

DEEP WOODS COVER 1/4 OF POLAND.

MASURIAN LAKES

OUR POPULATION IS 38 MILLION, 500 THOUSAND, AND WE SPEAK POLISH.

POLAND REACHED ITS PEAK OF POWER BETWEEN THE 14TH AND 17TH CENTURIES.

HAVING FEW NATURAL BOUNDARIES, POLAND HAS BEEN INVADED FROM BOTH EAST AND WEST AND HAS AT TIMES NOT EXISTED AS A SEPARATE COUNTRY.

VISTULA RIVER

ONE AREA IN POLAND HAS 485 SQUARE MILES OF THE LAST REMAINING LOWLAND PRIMEVAL FOREST IN CENTRAL EUROPE.

WARSAW

WOODEN WINDMILLS

ONE NATIONAL PARK IN POLAND HAS MORE THAN 1,800 SPECIES OF BUTTERFLIES.

SETTLED IN THE 11TH CENTURY, WARSAW IS KNOWN FOR ITS THEATER, MUSIC, AND ART.

INDUSTRY HERE INCLUDES MACHINERY, TEXTILES, IRON, STEEL, AND CHEMICALS.

POPULAR FOODS ARE KIELBASA (SPICY SAUSAGE) AND HAM.

WE ARE RICH IN COAL, NATURAL GAS, SULPHUR, AND COPPER.

CHAMOIS, (SMALL GOAT-LIKE ANTELOPE) BEARS, LYNX, WOLVES, EAGLES, AND BLACK STORKS LIVE HERE.

CZECH REPUBLIC

ELBE RV.

PRAGUE

SUGAR BEETS

BOHEMIA, IN THE WEST, IS A PLATEAU SURROUNDED BY FORESTS AND LOW MOUNTAINS.

CARPATHIAN MTS.

THE CITY OF KRAKOW HAS MANY BEAUTIFUL HISTORIC BUILDINGS.

VISTULA RIVER

BAA!

VLTAVA RIVER

WE HAVE COAL, TIMBER, AND URANIUM.

THE HILLY LAND OF MORAVIA IS AN IMPORTANT FARMING AREA.

OUR POPULATION IS 10 MILLION, 400 THOUSAND, AND OUR LANGUAGE IS CZECH.

ALMOST 50% OF OUR COUNTRY CONSISTS OF MOUNTAINS, FORESTS, AND PASTURES.

NORTH
WEST EAST
SOUTH

THIS HEAVILY INDUSTRIALIZED COUNTRY PRODUCES AUTOS, MACHINERY, CHEMICALS, ELECTRONICS AND MANY OTHER MANUFACTURED ITEMS.

SLOVAKIA

BRATISLAVA

METAL PROCESSING

BARLEY, SUGAR BEETS, PAPRIKA, AND MELONS ARE MAJOR AGRICULTURAL PRODUCTS.

RED PAPRIKA IS THE NATIONAL SPICE.

MT. KEKES 3,330 FT.

HUNGARY

BUDAPEST

LAKE BALATON IS THE LARGEST LAKE IN CENTRAL EUROPE.

AFTER BEING RULED BY THE AUSTRIAN EMPIRE FOR 300 YEARS, CZECH LANDS AND SLOVAKIA WERE UNITED TO FORM CZECHOSLOVAKIA IN 1918.

CZECHOSLOVAKIA SPLIT PEACEFULLY INTO THE CZECH REPUBLIC AND SLOVAKIA ON JANUARY 1, 1993.

PARLIAMENT BUILDINGS

PIANIST AND COMPOSER FRANZ LISZT WAS HUNGARIAN. HE CREATED THE SYMPHONIC POEM.

CHICKEN PAPRIKA IS ONE OF OUR FAMOUS DISHES.

DANUBE RIVER

Eastern Europe

At the end of World War II, part of Europe came under the control of the Soviet Union and became known as Eastern Europe. In the late 20th century, many Eastern European countries regained their independence.

Find out all about the countries of Eastern Europe, and where in the world they are. Then look for all of the following things, too.

- ☐ Barn
- ☐ Bear
- ☐ Bird
- ☐ Bison
- ☐ Butterflies (4)
- ☐ Carrot
- ☐ Cooks (3)
- ☐ Flower
- ☐ Hockey player
- ☐ Music notes
- ☐ Pigs (2)
- ☐ Radio tower
- ☐ Sausage
- ☐ Scarecrows (5)
- ☐ Sheep
- ☐ Tennis ball
- ☐ Tourists
- ☐ Truck
- ☐ Windmill
- ☐ Woolly mammoth

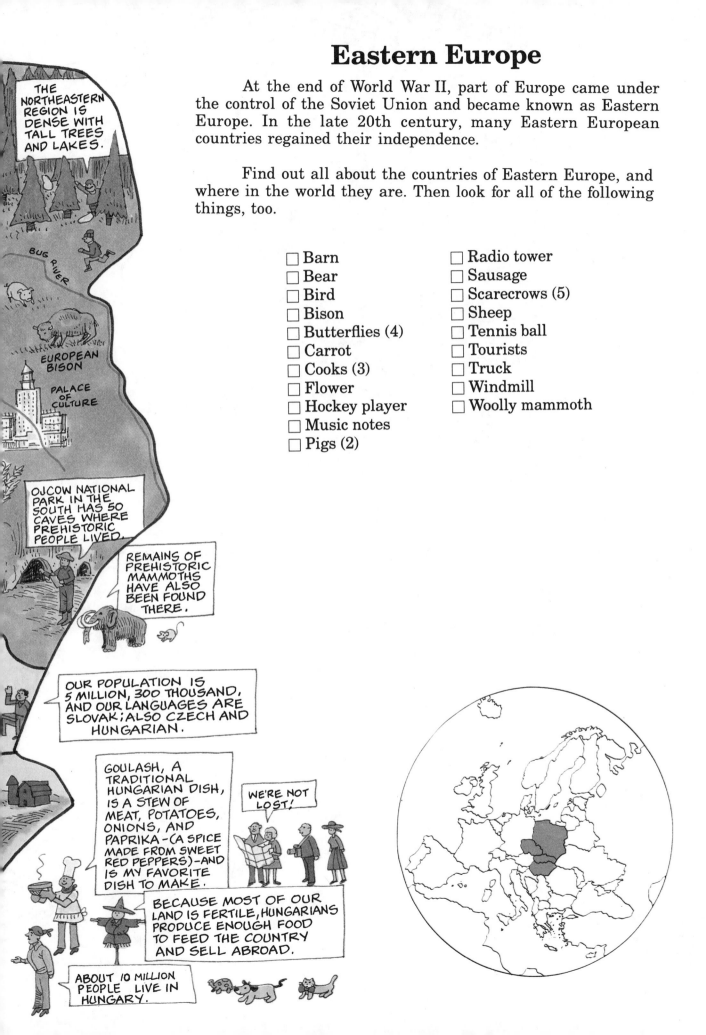

THE NORTHEASTERN REGION IS DENSE WITH TALL TREES AND LAKES.

BUG RIVER

EUROPEAN BISON

PALACE OF CULTURE

OJCOW NATIONAL PARK IN THE SOUTH HAS 50 CAVES WHERE PREHISTORIC PEOPLE LIVED.

REMAINS OF PREHISTORIC MAMMOTHS HAVE ALSO BEEN FOUND THERE.

OUR POPULATION IS 5 MILLION, 300 THOUSAND, AND OUR LANGUAGES ARE SLOVAK; ALSO CZECH AND HUNGARIAN.

GOULASH, A TRADITIONAL HUNGARIAN DISH, IS A STEW OF MEAT, POTATOES, ONIONS, AND PAPRIKA - (A SPICE MADE FROM SWEET RED PEPPERS) - AND IS MY FAVORITE DISH TO MAKE.

WE'RE NOT LOST!

BECAUSE MOST OF OUR LAND IS FERTILE, HUNGARIANS PRODUCE ENOUGH FOOD TO FEED THE COUNTRY AND SELL ABROAD.

ABOUT 10 MILLION PEOPLE LIVE IN HUNGARY.

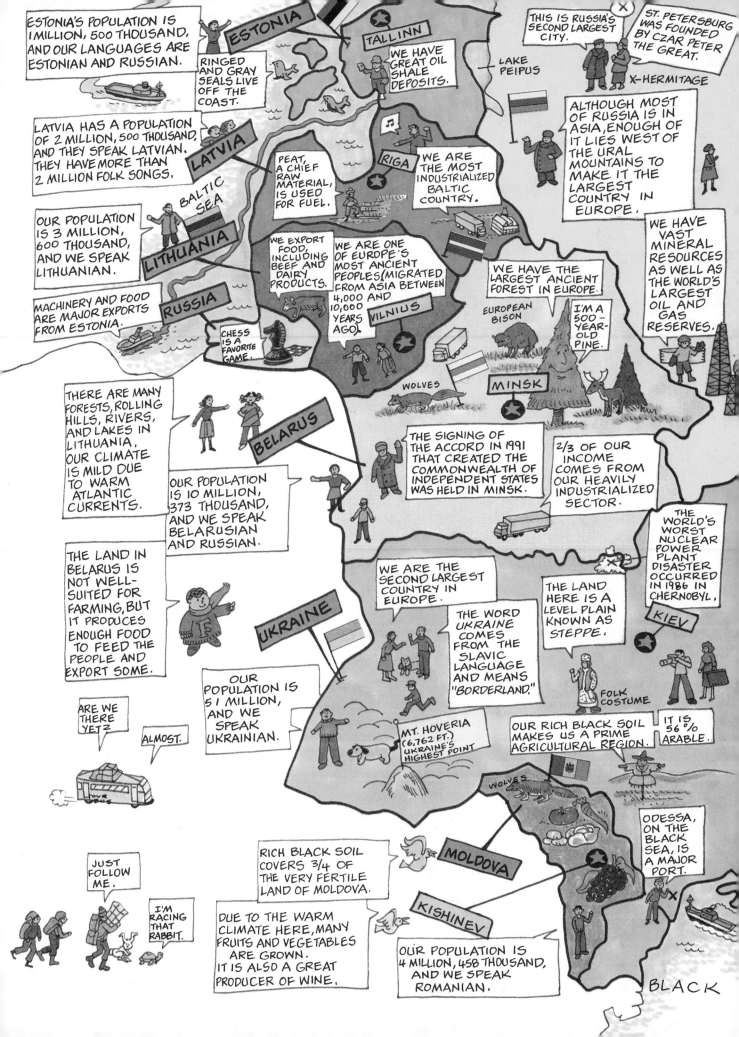

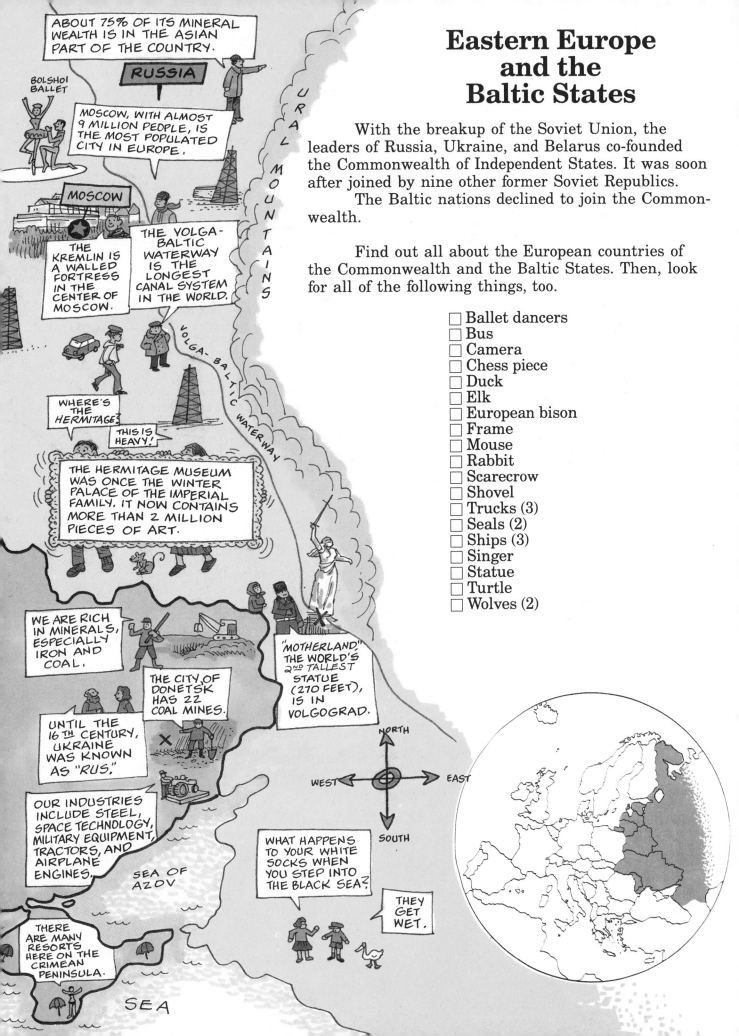

Eastern Europe and the Baltic States

With the breakup of the Soviet Union, the leaders of Russia, Ukraine, and Belarus co-founded the Commonwealth of Independent States. It was soon after joined by nine other former Soviet Republics.

The Baltic nations declined to join the Commonwealth.

Find out all about the European countries of the Commonwealth and the Baltic States. Then, look for all of the following things, too.

☐ Ballet dancers
☐ Bus
☐ Camera
☐ Chess piece
☐ Duck
☐ Elk
☐ European bison
☐ Frame
☐ Mouse
☐ Rabbit
☐ Scarecrow
☐ Shovel
☐ Trucks (3)
☐ Seals (2)
☐ Ships (3)
☐ Singer
☐ Statue
☐ Turtle
☐ Wolves (2)

The Balkan States

Much of the land known as the Balkan states was ruled by Turkey from the end of the 15th century until 1913. After the end of World War I, the Balkan country of Yugoslavia was created when several regions were combined into a federation of six republics. Divided by nationalistic and religious differences, the republics began to separate into independent nations in 1991. Former Yugoslavia consists of Serbia and Montenegro, Slovenia, Croatia, Bosnia and Herzegovina, and Macedonia.

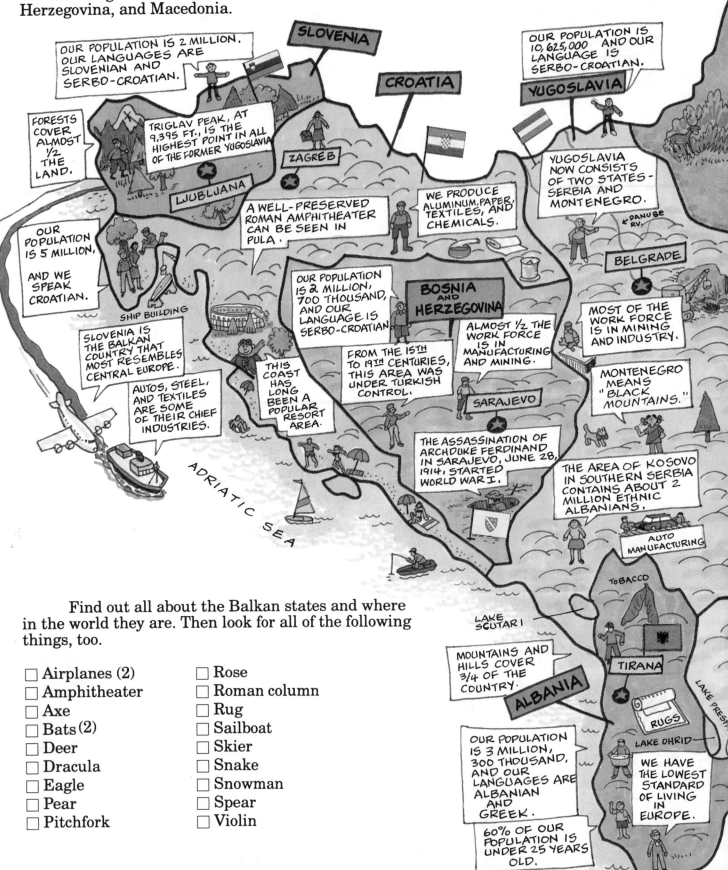

SLOVENIA

OUR POPULATION IS 2 MILLION. OUR LANGUAGES ARE SLOVENIAN AND SERBO-CROATIAN.

CROATIA

OUR POPULATION IS 10,625,000 AND OUR LANGUAGE IS SERBO-CROATIAN.

YUGOSLAVIA

FORESTS COVER ALMOST 1/2 THE LAND.

TRIGLAV PEAK, AT 9,395 FT., IS THE HIGHEST POINT IN ALL OF THE FORMER YUGOSLAVIA.

ZAGREB

YUGOSLAVIA NOW CONSISTS OF TWO STATES - SERBIA AND MONTENEGRO.

DANUBE RV.

LJUBLJANA

A WELL-PRESERVED ROMAN AMPHITHEATER CAN BE SEEN IN PULA.

WE PRODUCE ALUMINUM, PAPER, TEXTILES, AND CHEMICALS.

BELGRADE

OUR POPULATION IS 5 MILLION, AND WE SPEAK CROATIAN.

SHIP BUILDING

OUR POPULATION IS 2 MILLION, 700 THOUSAND, AND OUR LANGUAGE IS SERBO-CROATIAN.

BOSNIA AND HERZEGOVINA

MOST OF THE WORK FORCE IS IN MINING AND INDUSTRY.

SLOVENIA IS THE BALKAN COUNTRY THAT MOST RESEMBLES CENTRAL EUROPE.

ALMOST 1/2 THE WORK FORCE IS IN MANUFACTURING AND MINING.

MONTENEGRO MEANS "BLACK MOUNTAINS."

AUTOS, STEEL, AND TEXTILES ARE SOME OF THEIR CHIEF INDUSTRIES.

THIS COAST HAS LONG BEEN A POPULAR RESORT AREA.

FROM THE 15TH TO 19TH CENTURIES, THIS AREA WAS UNDER TURKISH CONTROL.

SARAJEVO

THE ASSASSINATION OF ARCHDUKE FERDINAND IN SARAJEVO, JUNE 28, 1914, STARTED WORLD WAR I.

THE AREA OF KOSOVO IN SOUTHERN SERBIA CONTAINS ABOUT 2 MILLION ETHNIC ALBANIANS.

ADRIATIC SEA

AUTO MANUFACTURING

TOBACCO

LAKE SCUTARI

Find out all about the Balkan states and where in the world they are. Then look for all of the following things, too.

MOUNTAINS AND HILLS COVER 3/4 OF THE COUNTRY.

TIRANA

ALBANIA

LAKE PRESP

RUGS

LAKE OHRID

WE HAVE THE LOWEST STANDARD OF LIVING IN EUROPE.

OUR POPULATION IS 3 MILLION, 300 THOUSAND, AND OUR LANGUAGES ARE ALBANIAN AND GREEK.

60% OF OUR POPULATION IS UNDER 25 YEARS OLD.

- ☐ Airplanes (2)
- ☐ Amphitheater
- ☐ Axe
- ☐ Bats (2)
- ☐ Deer
- ☐ Dracula
- ☐ Eagle
- ☐ Pear
- ☐ Pitchfork
- ☐ Rose
- ☐ Roman column
- ☐ Rug
- ☐ Sailboat
- ☐ Skier
- ☐ Snake
- ☐ Snowman
- ☐ Spear
- ☐ Violin

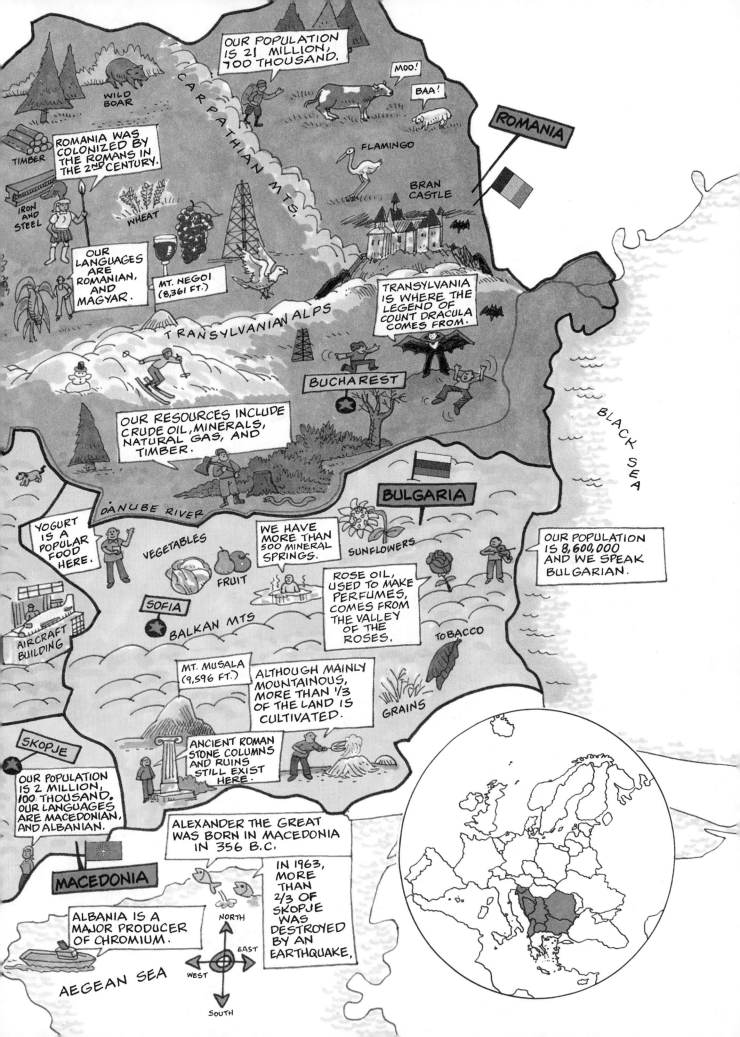

Greece

The ideals of western democracy were born in Greece about 2,500 years ago. The art, philosophy, theater, mythology, science, and architecture that flourished there formed the basis of western civilization.

Find out all about Greece and where in the world it is. Then look for all of the following things, too.

☐ Book   ☐ Dolphin   ☐ Olympic torch bearer
☐ Camera   ☐ Grapes   ☐ Sailboat
☐ Cotton   ☐ Octopus   ☐ Vase

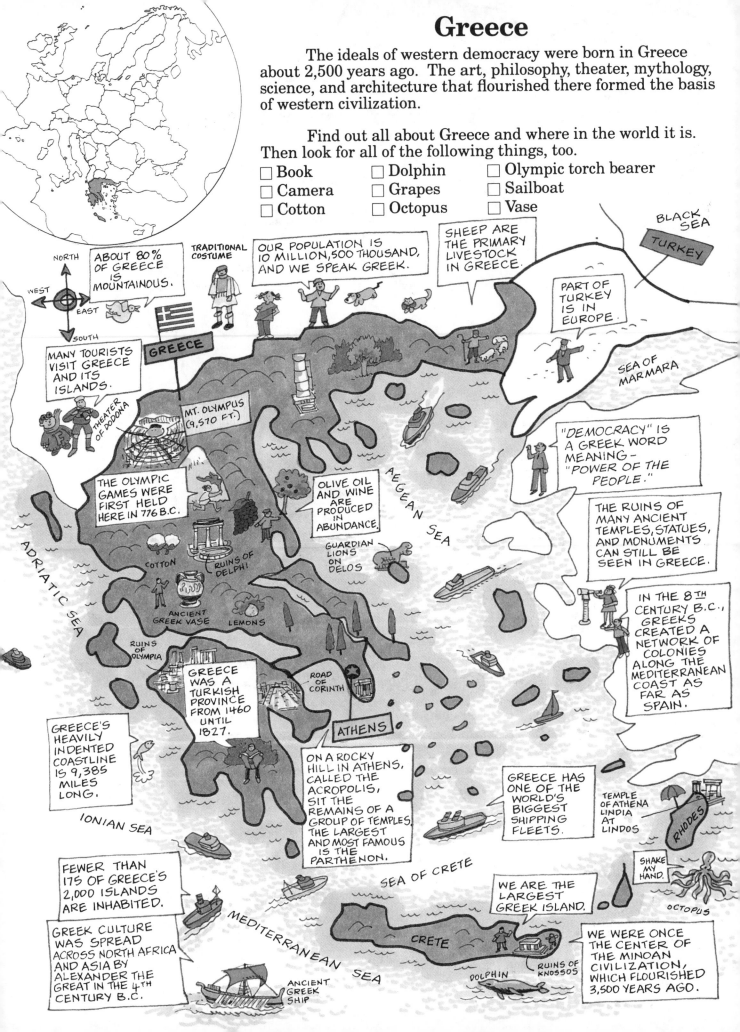

BLACK SEA

TURKEY

TRADITIONAL COSTUME

NORTH
WEST
EAST
SOUTH

ABOUT 80% OF GREECE IS MOUNTAINOUS.

OUR POPULATION IS 10 MILLION, 500 THOUSAND, AND WE SPEAK GREEK.

SHEEP ARE THE PRIMARY LIVESTOCK IN GREECE.

PART OF TURKEY IS IN EUROPE.

SEA OF MARMARA

GREECE

MANY TOURISTS VISIT GREECE AND ITS ISLANDS.

THEATER OF DODONA

MT. OLYMPUS (9,570 FT.)

"DEMOCRACY" IS A GREEK WORD MEANING - "POWER OF THE PEOPLE."

AEGEAN SEA

THE OLYMPIC GAMES WERE FIRST HELD HERE IN 776 B.C.

OLIVE OIL AND WINE ARE PRODUCED IN ABUNDANCE.

THE RUINS OF MANY ANCIENT TEMPLES, STATUES, AND MONUMENTS CAN STILL BE SEEN IN GREECE.

GUARDIAN LIONS ON DELOS

COTTON

RUINS OF DELPHI

ANCIENT GREEK VASE

LEMONS

IN THE 8TH CENTURY B.C., GREEKS CREATED A NETWORK OF COLONIES ALONG THE MEDITERRANEAN COAST AS FAR AS SPAIN.

ADRIATIC SEA

RUINS OF OLYMPIA

GREECE WAS A TURKISH PROVINCE FROM 1460 UNTIL 1827.

ROAD OF CORINTH

ATHENS

GREECE'S HEAVILY INDENTED COASTLINE IS 9,385 MILES LONG.

ON A ROCKY HILL IN ATHENS, CALLED THE ACROPOLIS, SIT THE REMAINS OF A GROUP OF TEMPLES, THE LARGEST AND MOST FAMOUS IS THE PARTHENON.

GREECE HAS ONE OF THE WORLD'S BIGGEST SHIPPING FLEETS.

TEMPLE OF ATHENA LINDIA AT LINDOS

RHODES

SHAKE MY HAND.

IONIAN SEA

FEWER THAN 175 OF GREECE'S 2,000 ISLANDS ARE INHABITED.

SEA OF CRETE

WE ARE THE LARGEST GREEK ISLAND.

OCTOPUS

GREEK CULTURE WAS SPREAD ACROSS NORTH AFRICA AND ASIA BY ALEXANDER THE GREAT IN THE 4TH CENTURY B.C.

MEDITERRANEAN SEA

CRETE

ANCIENT GREEK SHIP

DOLPHIN

RUINS OF KNOSSOS

WE WERE ONCE THE CENTER OF THE MINOAN CIVILIZATION, WHICH FLOURISHED 3,500 YEARS AGO.

AFRICA

III

Search and find lots of interesting facts about:

- **North Africa**
- **The Sahel**
- **The Western Coast**
- **Central Africa**
- **The Horn of Africa**

- **Equatorial Africa**
- **East Africa**
- **Southern Africa**
- **The Cape of Africa**
- **The Island Nations**

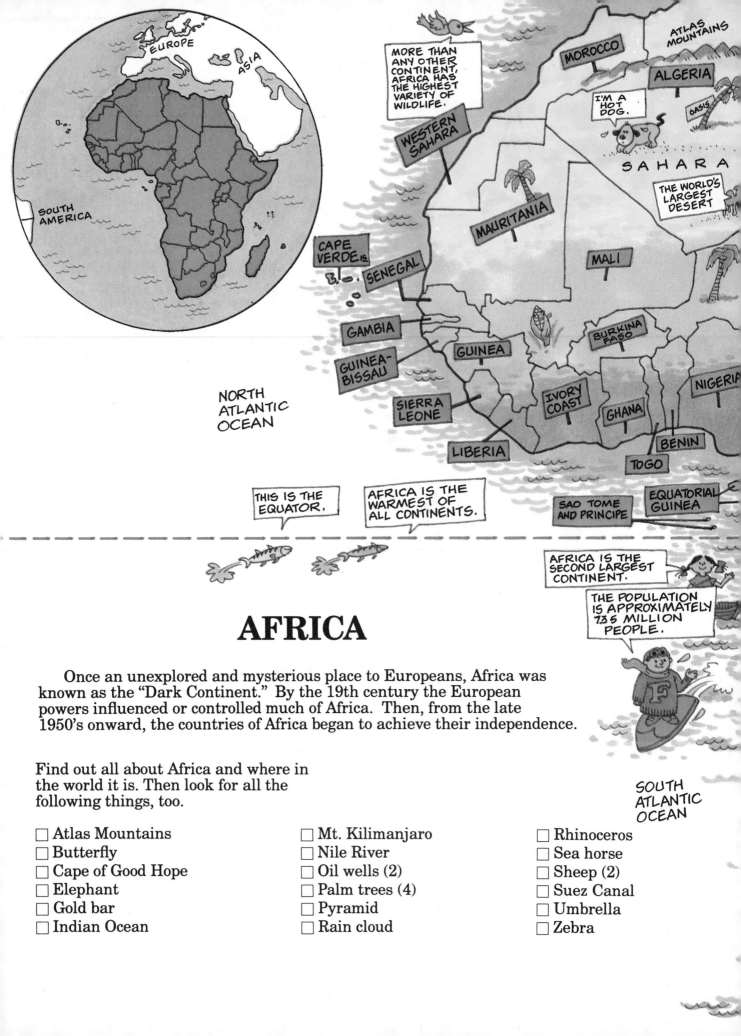

AFRICA

Once an unexplored and mysterious place to Europeans, Africa was known as the "Dark Continent." By the 19th century the European powers influenced or controlled much of Africa. Then, from the late 1950's onward, the countries of Africa began to achieve their independence.

Find out all about Africa and where in the world it is. Then look for all the following things, too.

- ☐ Atlas Mountains
- ☐ Butterfly
- ☐ Cape of Good Hope
- ☐ Elephant
- ☐ Gold bar
- ☐ Indian Ocean

- ☐ Mt. Kilimanjaro
- ☐ Nile River
- ☐ Oil wells (2)
- ☐ Palm trees (4)
- ☐ Pyramid
- ☐ Rain cloud

- ☐ Rhinoceros
- ☐ Sea horse
- ☐ Sheep (2)
- ☐ Suez Canal
- ☐ Umbrella
- ☐ Zebra

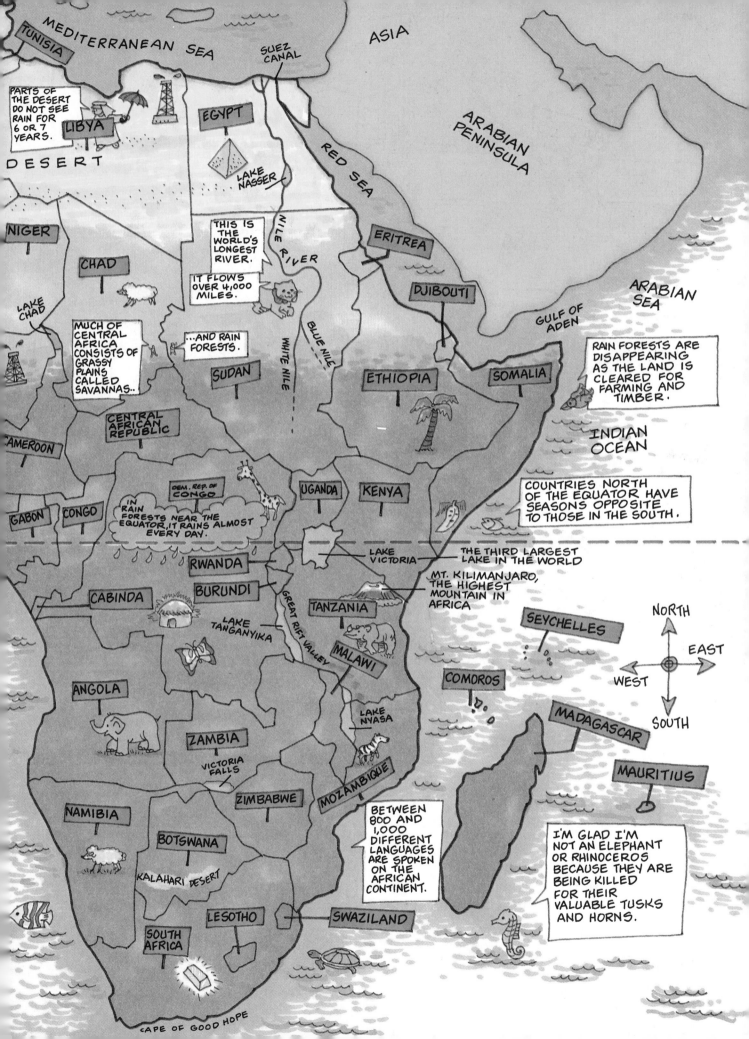

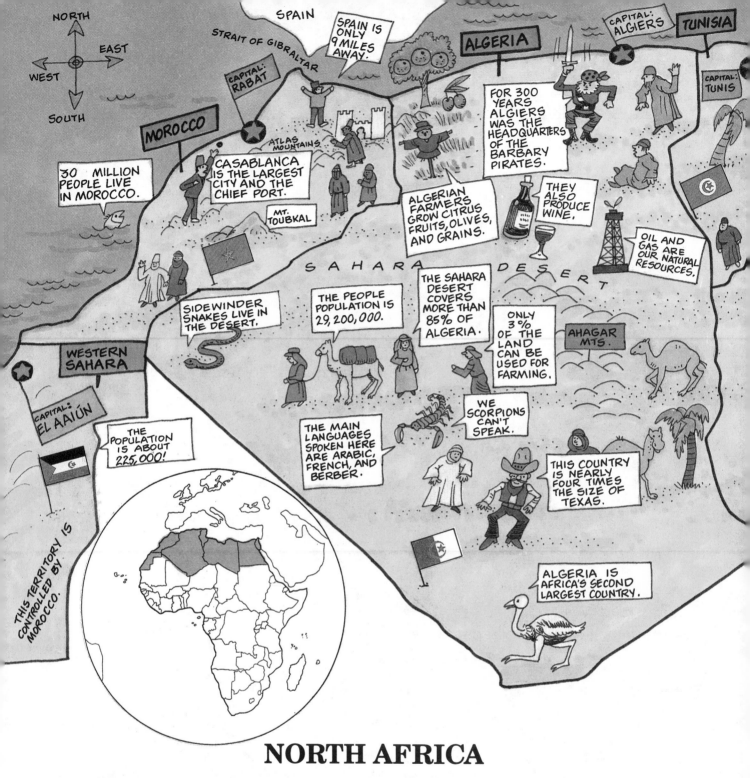

NORTH AFRICA

North of the Sahara, ancient Egyptians, Greeks, Romans, and peoples of Arabia have influenced African cultures. Today, in North Africa, the Arabic language is dominant and the major religion is Islam.

Find out all about North Africa
and where in the world it is. Then
look for all the following things, too.

- ☐ Barbary ape
- ☐ Beret
- ☐ Boats (3)
- ☐ Bunch of grapes
- ☐ Hyena
- ☐ Miner
- ☐ Orange tree
- ☐ Oil wells (4)
- ☐ Ostrich
- ☐ Pencil
- ☐ Pirate
- ☐ Pyramids (4)
- ☐ Scarecrow
- ☐ Scorpion
- ☐ Shovel
- ☐ Snake
- ☐ Thermometer

THE SAHEL

Below the deserts of North Africa is the Sahel, a region long inhabited by animal grazers and farmers. As the Sahara expands south — about 3 miles each year — much of the Sahel is becoming part of the desert.

Find out all about the Sahel and where in the world it is. Then look for all the following things, too.

- ☐ Anchor
- ☐ Basket
- ☐ Bird
- ☐ Camels (5)
- ☐ Cotton balls (3)
- ☐ Goat
- ☐ Elephant
- ☐ Fisherman
- ☐ Hippopotamus
- ☐ Lake Chad
- ☐ Niger River
- ☐ Peanuts (3)
- ☐ Periscope
- ☐ Soccer ball
- ☐ Sun
- ☐ Tent

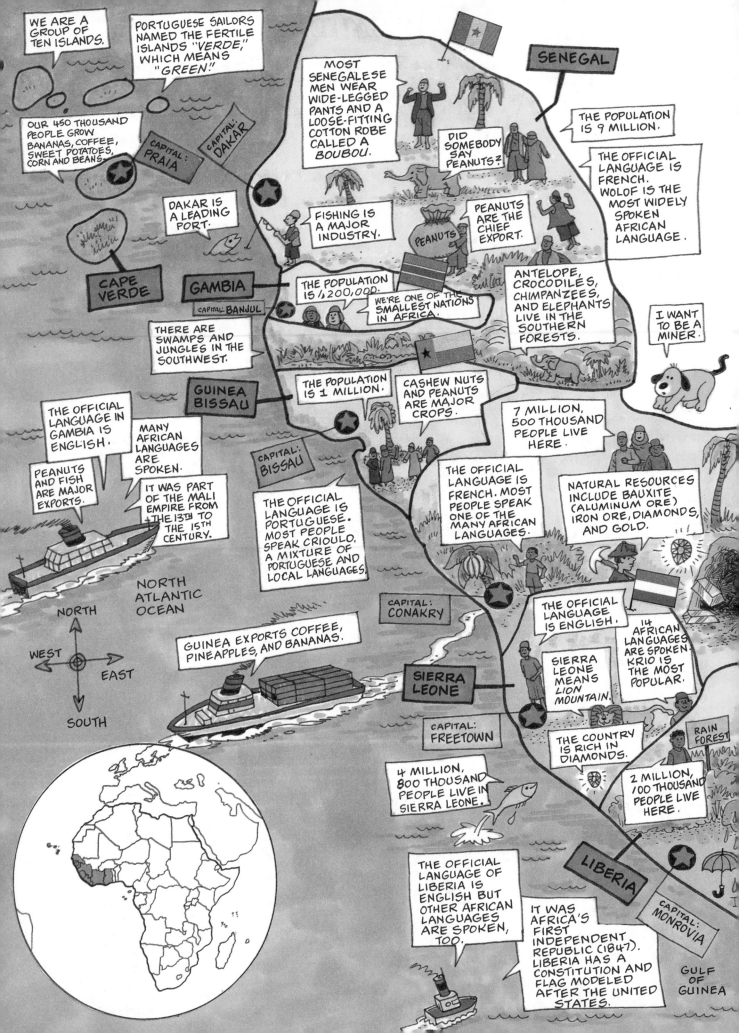

THE WESTERN COAST

The landscape of the western coast of Africa varies from humid coastal plains and swamps to forested hills and plateaus. The soil is fertile, and crops such as cocoa, coffee, and peanuts are grown.

During the era of the slave trade to the Americas, and for centuries before with other nations, coastal kingdoms of West Africa grew rich by trading slaves, gold, and ivory.

Find out all about the western coast of Africa and where in the world it is. Then look for all the following things, too.

- ☐ Boats (4)
- ☐ Chocolate bar
- ☐ Coffeepot
- ☐ Crocodile
- ☐ Diamonds (4)
- ☐ Elephants (4)
- ☐ Fisherman
- ☐ Game warden
- ☐ Gold bars (3)
- ☐ Lake Volta
- ☐ Lion
- ☐ Miner
- ☐ Pygmy hippopotamus
- ☐ Rain clouds (2)
- ☐ Umbrella

GUINEA

I'D LIKE A CHOCOLATE BAR.

I LOVE PEANUTS.

GHANA

I SEE A CUTE LION.

IVORY COAST

THE POPULATION IS 17,700,000.

THE OFFICIAL LANGUAGE IS ENGLISH BUT THERE ARE MANY AFRICAN LANGUAGES SPOKEN HERE.

HISTORY IS RECITED BY STORY-TELLERS CALLED GRIOTS.

THE POPULATION IS 14,800,000.

WE EXPORT COFFEE, COCOA, AND TROPICAL WOODS.

COCOA BEANS

THE OFFICIAL LANGUAGE IS FRENCH. AFRICAN LANGUAGES INCLUDE DIOULA, BAOULE, AND BETE.

BEFORE GAINING INDEPENDENCE FROM GREAT BRITAIN IN 1957, GHANA USED TO BE KNOWN AS THE GOLD COAST.

CAPITAL: ABIDJAN

THE COUNTRY WAS NAMED FOR THE IVORY TRADE WHICH FLOURISHED FROM THE 13TH TO EARLY 20TH CENTURY.

LAKE VOLTA

AN ENDANGERED SPECIES, THE PYGMY HIPPOPOTAMUS LIVES IN THE MARSHY SOUTHERN AREA OF GHANA.

RAIN FOREST

TODAY, IVORY TRADE IS ILLEGAL, AND THE NATION PROTECTS ITS ELEPHANTS IN GAME PRESERVES.

NATURAL RESOURCES INCLUDE GOLD, DIAMONDS, AND FISH.

SOME OF THE LOCAL LANGUAGES HAVE NO SOUND FOR "R" BUT USE "L" INSTEAD. SO ACCRA IS PRONOUNCED "ACCLA".

WE GET 160 INCHES OF RAIN EACH YEAR.

LIBERIA WAS FOUNDED FOR THE SETTLEMENT OF FREED AMERICAN SLAVES.

NO HUNTING

IT'S SAFE HERE.

CHOCOLATE

CAPITAL: ACCRA

COCOA BEANS ARE THE NUMBER ONE EXPORT.

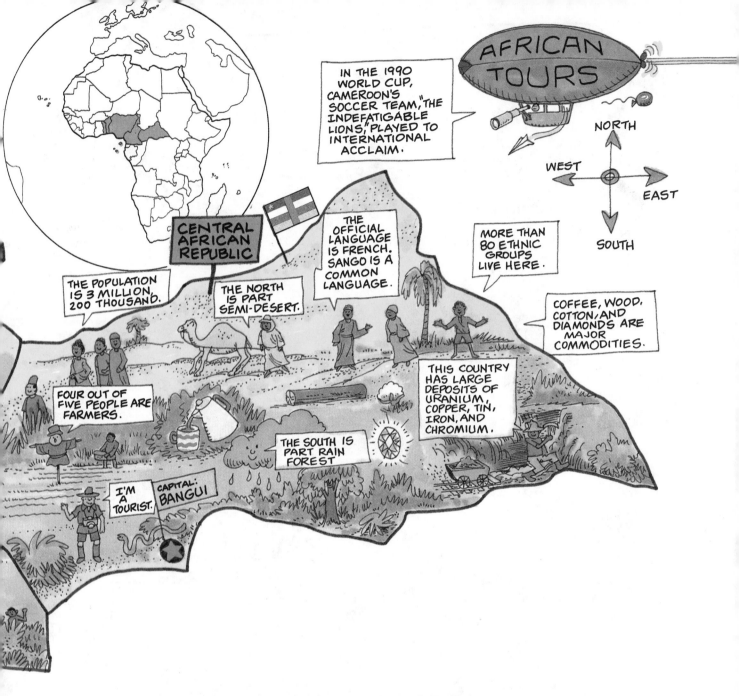

CENTRAL AFRICA

The countries on the Gulf of Guinea share part of the old "slave coast." Their landscape is incredibly varied, with old volcanic mountains, semi-desert regions, savannas, swamps, and tropical rain forests.

Find out all about the countries of central Africa and where in the world they are. Then look for all the following things, too.

- ☐ Camera
- ☐ Cup
- ☐ Fishing poles (2)
- ☐ Giraffe
- ☐ Huts (2)
- ☐ Life preserver
- ☐ Oil wells (3)
- ☐ Paper airplane
- ☐ Red car
- ☐ Scarecrow
- ☐ Shark
- ☐ Snakes (2)
- ☐ Telescope
- ☐ Umbrellas (2)
- ☐ Volcano

THE HORN OF AFRICA

The region on the eastern coast is known as the Horn of Africa. On the map, it looks like the horn of a rhinoceros jutting into the Indian Ocean.

Find out all about the Horn of Africa and where in the world it is. Then look for all the following things, too.

- ☐ Aardvark
- ☐ Acacia tree
- ☐ Banana
- ☐ Coffeepot
- ☐ Cotton
- ☐ Giraffes (2)
- ☐ Horseshoe
- ☐ Lion
- ☐ Marshmallow
- ☐ Nile crocodile
- ☐ Nubian Desert
- ☐ Oryx
- ☐ Ostrich
- ☐ Red Sea
- ☐ Umbrella
- ☐ White Nile
- ☐ Zebra

WHAT HAPPENS IF YOU THROW A WHITE STONE INTO THE RED SEA?

IT GETS WET.

DJIBOUTI

THIS COUNTRY IS ONE OF THE HOTTEST AND DRIEST SPOTS ON EARTH.

THE POPULATION IS 425 THOUSAND.

CAPITAL: DJIBOUTI

GULF OF ADEN

THE POPULATION IS 9 MILLION, 7'00 THOUSAND.

SOMALIA

I'M AN ORYX AND YOU'RE NOT.

THE OFFICIAL LANGUAGE IS SOMALI. ENGLISH IS USED IN THE NORTH, AND ITALIAN IN THE SOUTH.

THE OFFICIAL LANGUAGES OF DJIBOUTI ARE FRENCH AND ARABIC. AFAR AND SOMALIA ARE ALSO SPOKEN.

THEY HAVE NO ARABLE LAND. SALT IS THEIR PRINCIPAL NATURAL RESOURCE.

EARTHQUAKES OFTEN SHAKE THE GREAT RIFT VALLEY, WHICH RUNS THROUGH ETHIOPIA!

THE OFFICIAL LANGUAGE IS AMHARIC, RELATED TO THE ANCIENT PHOENICIAN LANGUAGE.

SOMALIA IS THE EASTERNMOST COUNTRY ON THE CONTINENT.

MANY ETHIOPIANS WEAR "SHAMAS", A ONE-PIECE CLOTH OF THIN WHITE FABRIC.

IT IS SLIGHTLY SMALLER THAN TEXAS.

INDIAN OCEAN

I'M AN ACACIA TREE.

LIVESTOCK, BANANAS, HIDES, AND FISH ARE MAJOR PRODUCTS.

MOST SOMALIS BELONG TO ONE OF THE FOUR CLANS THAT MAKE UP THE SAMAAL. THEY WERE ONCE PRIMARILY NOMADS.

AFTER A 30 YEAR STRUGGLE FOR INDEPENDENCE FROM ETHIOPIA, ERITREA BECAME AN INDEPENDENT NATION IN 1993.

ITALY COLONIZED ERITREA FROM THE LATE 1800s UNTIL THE END OF WORLD WAR II.

I'M HOT!

TWO OTHER CLANS, CALLED SAAB, ARE MAINLY FARMERS LIVING ALONG THE RIVERS IN SOUTHERN SOMALIA.

CAPITAL: MOGADISHU

I'M A HOT DOG!

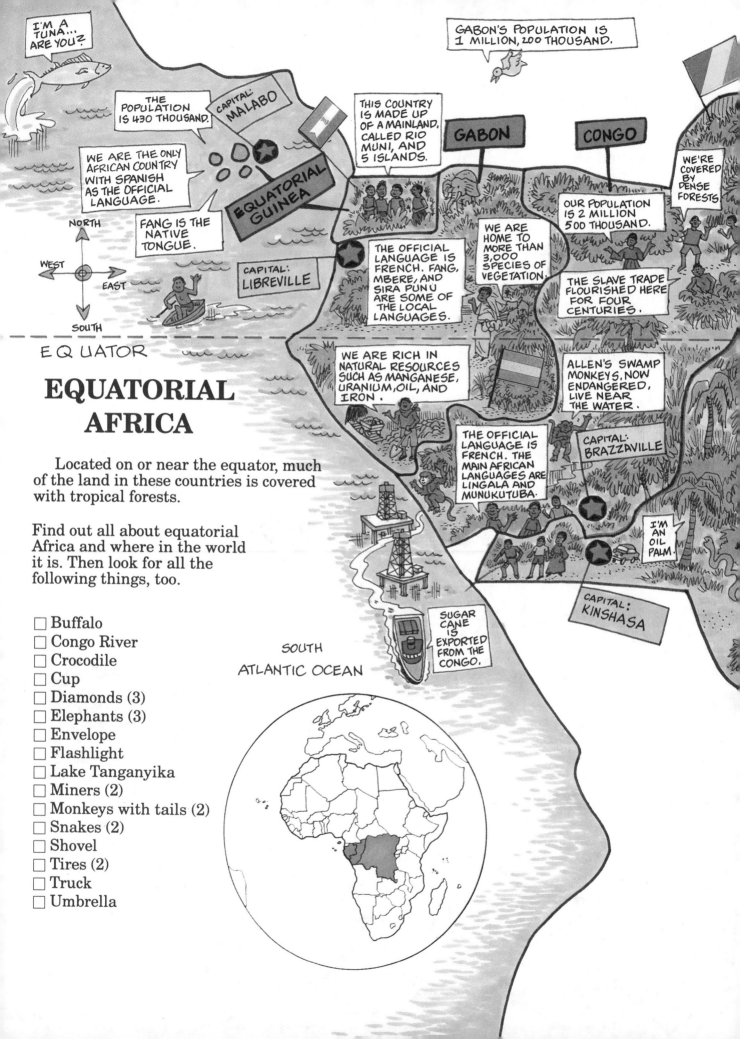

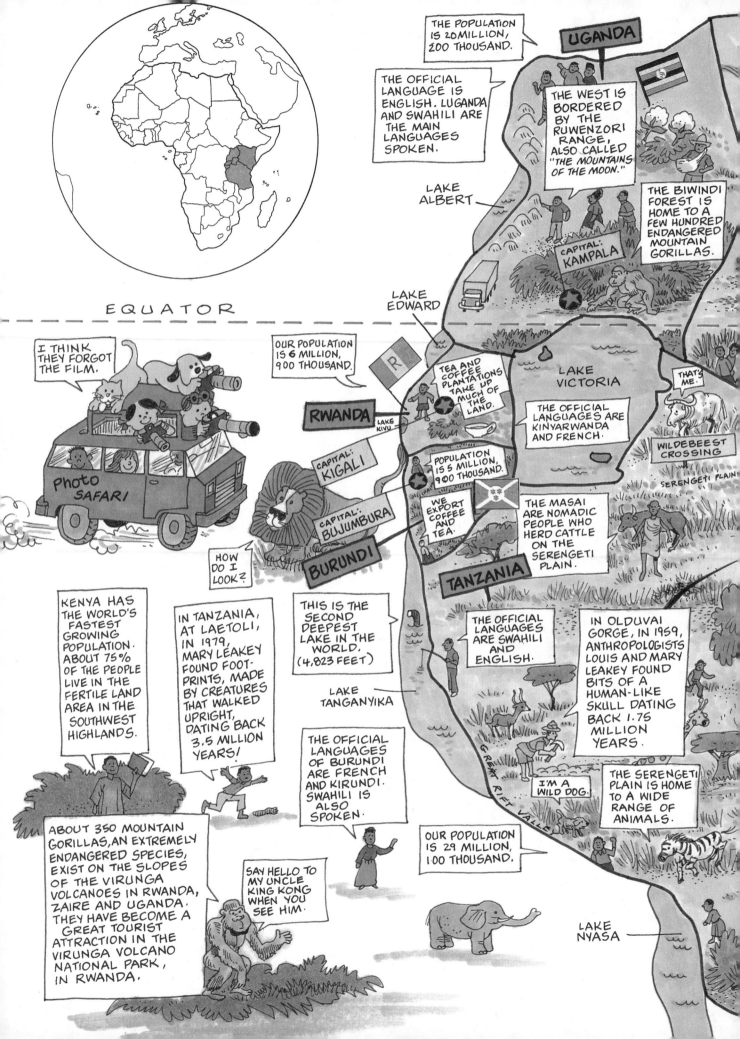

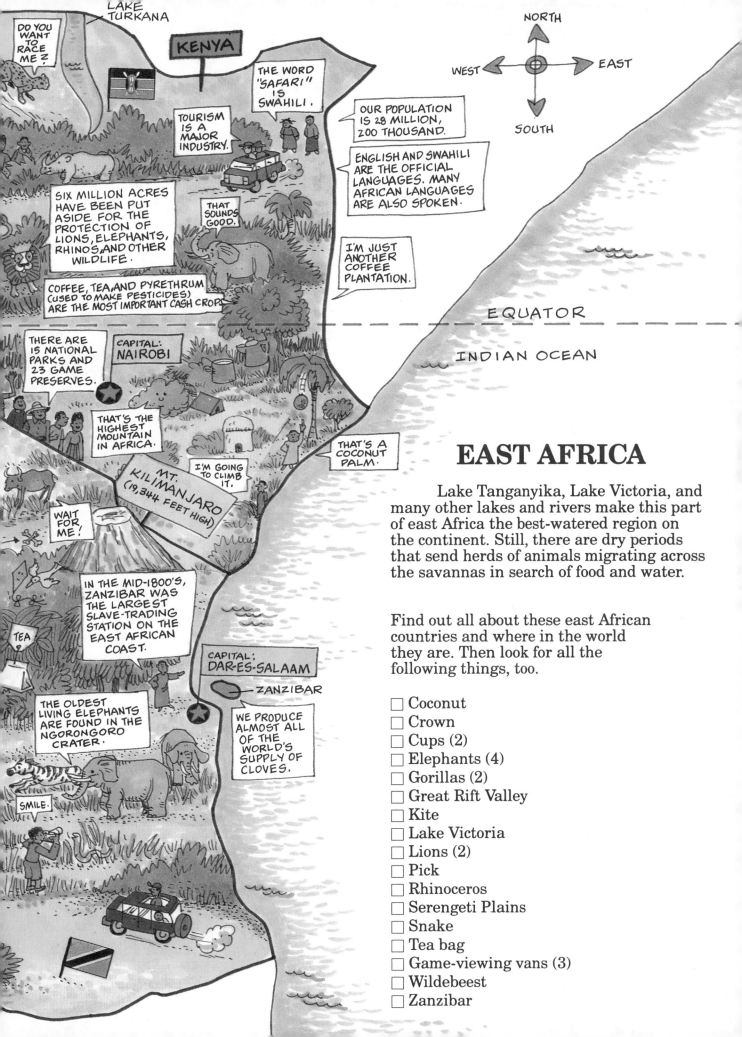

EAST AFRICA

Lake Tanganyika, Lake Victoria, and many other lakes and rivers make this part of east Africa the best-watered region on the continent. Still, there are dry periods that send herds of animals migrating across the savannas in search of food and water.

Find out all about these east African countries and where in the world they are. Then look for all the following things, too.

- ☐ Coconut
- ☐ Crown
- ☐ Cups (2)
- ☐ Elephants (4)
- ☐ Gorillas (2)
- ☐ Great Rift Valley
- ☐ Kite
- ☐ Lake Victoria
- ☐ Lions (2)
- ☐ Pick
- ☐ Rhinoceros
- ☐ Serengeti Plains
- ☐ Snake
- ☐ Tea bag
- ☐ Game-viewing vans (3)
- ☐ Wildebeest
- ☐ Zanzibar

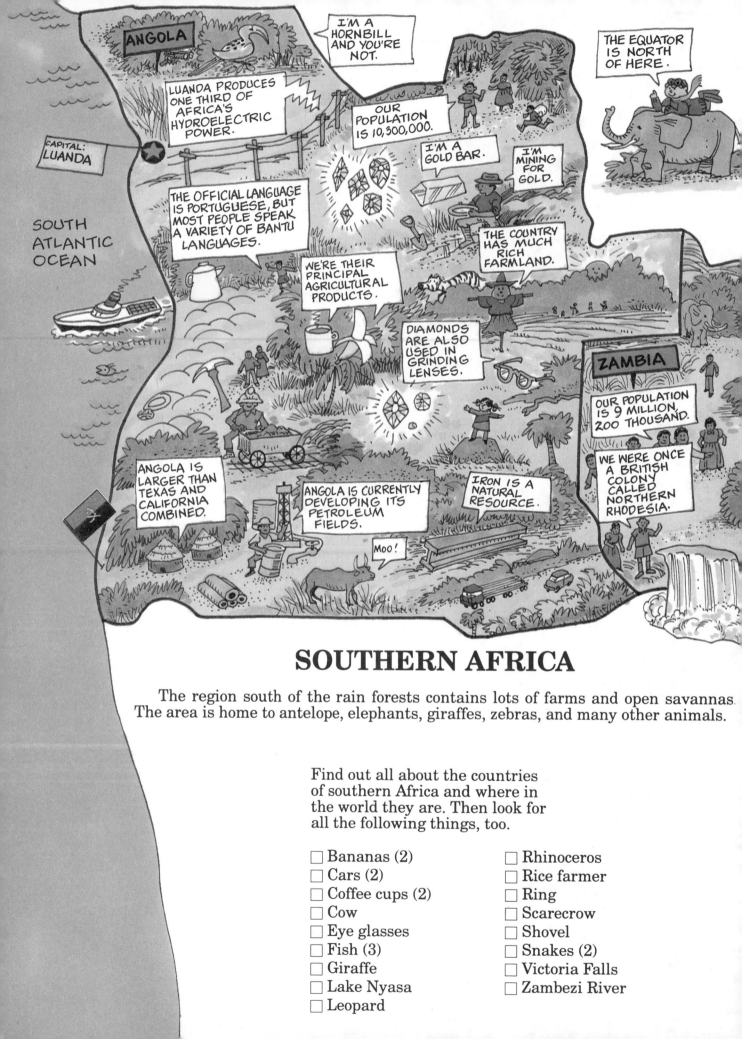

SOUTHERN AFRICA

The region south of the rain forests contains lots of farms and open savannas. The area is home to antelope, elephants, giraffes, zebras, and many other animals.

Find out all about the countries of southern Africa and where in the world they are. Then look for all the following things, too.

- ☐ Bananas (2)
- ☐ Cars (2)
- ☐ Coffee cups (2)
- ☐ Cow
- ☐ Eye glasses
- ☐ Fish (3)
- ☐ Giraffe
- ☐ Lake Nyasa
- ☐ Leopard
- ☐ Rhinoceros
- ☐ Rice farmer
- ☐ Ring
- ☐ Scarecrow
- ☐ Shovel
- ☐ Snakes (2)
- ☐ Victoria Falls
- ☐ Zambezi River

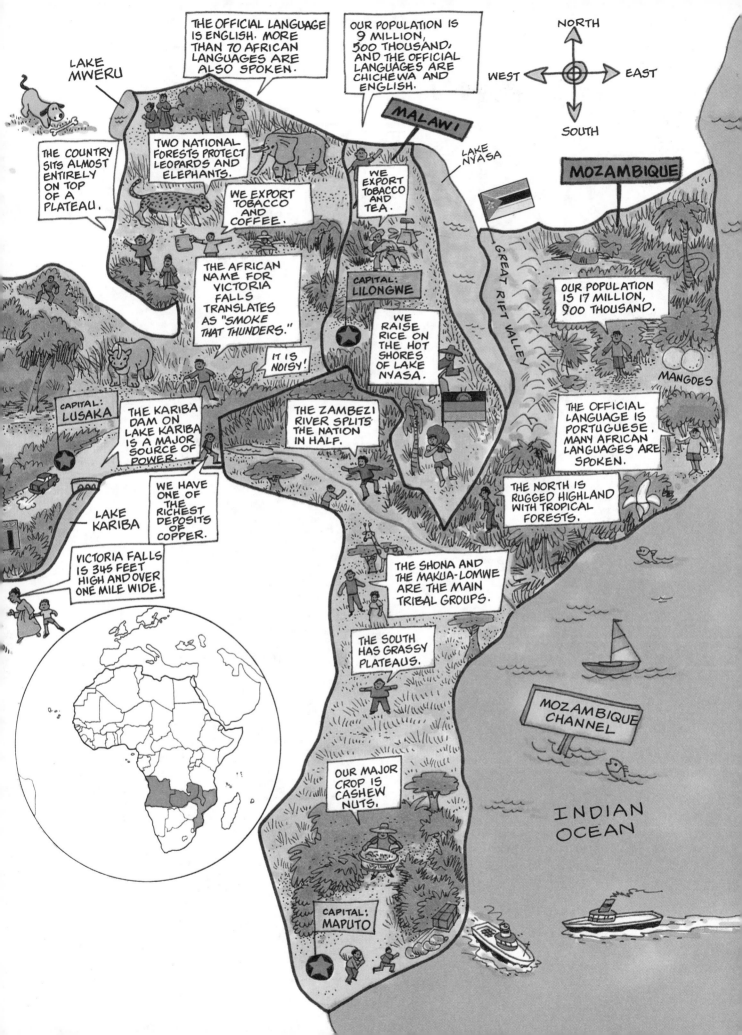

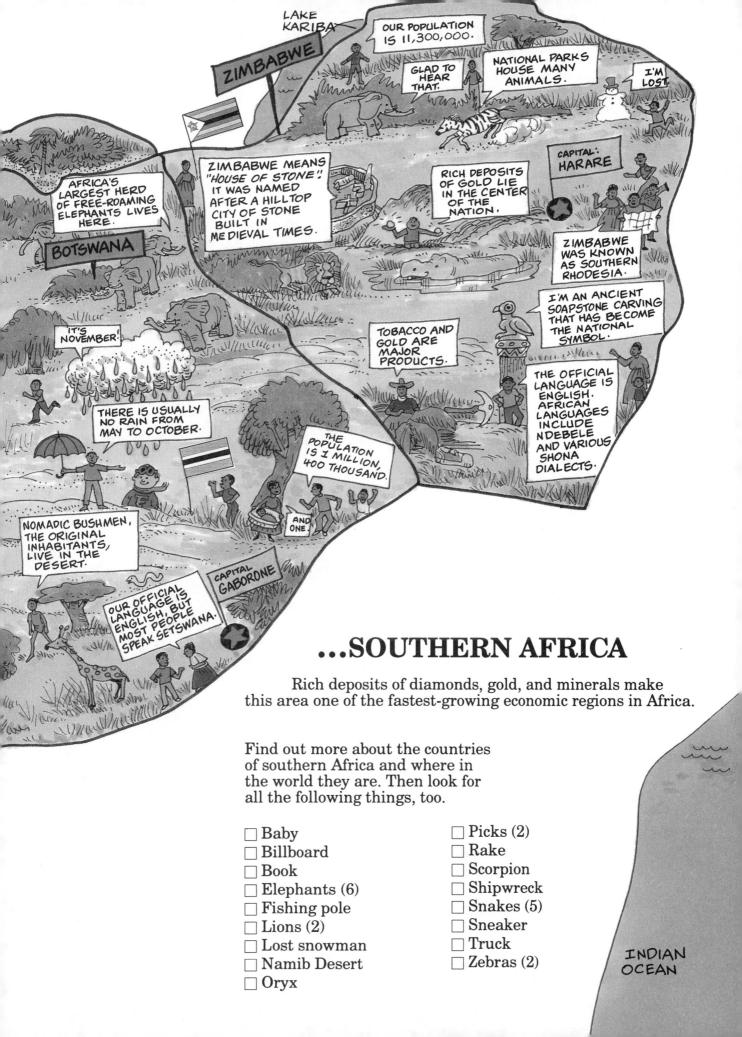

...SOUTHERN AFRICA

Rich deposits of diamonds, gold, and minerals make this area one of the fastest-growing economic regions in Africa.

Find out more about the countries of southern Africa and where in the world they are. Then look for all the following things, too.

- ☐ Baby
- ☐ Billboard
- ☐ Book
- ☐ Elephants (6)
- ☐ Fishing pole
- ☐ Lions (2)
- ☐ Lost snowman
- ☐ Namib Desert
- ☐ Oryx
- ☐ Picks (2)
- ☐ Rake
- ☐ Scorpion
- ☐ Shipwreck
- ☐ Snakes (5)
- ☐ Sneaker
- ☐ Truck
- ☐ Zebras (2)

THE CAPE OF AFRICA

The world's greatest diamond and gold mines are in South Africa, making it the richest country in Africa. The mines employ tens of thousands of men from neighboring countries.

Find out all about the cape of Africa and where in the world it is. Then look for all the following things, too.

- ☐ Cars (4)
- ☐ Citrus fruit
- ☐ Crown
- ☐ Drummer
- ☐ Giraffes (3)
- ☐ Grapes
- ☐ Guitar
- ☐ Lion
- ☐ Orange River
- ☐ Ostrich
- ☐ Pineapple
- ☐ Sailor
- ☐ Scarecrow
- ☐ Sheep (2)
- ☐ Shovel
- ☐ Table Mountain
- ☐ Tent
- ☐ Tractor
- ☐ Zebra
- ☐ Zulu warrior

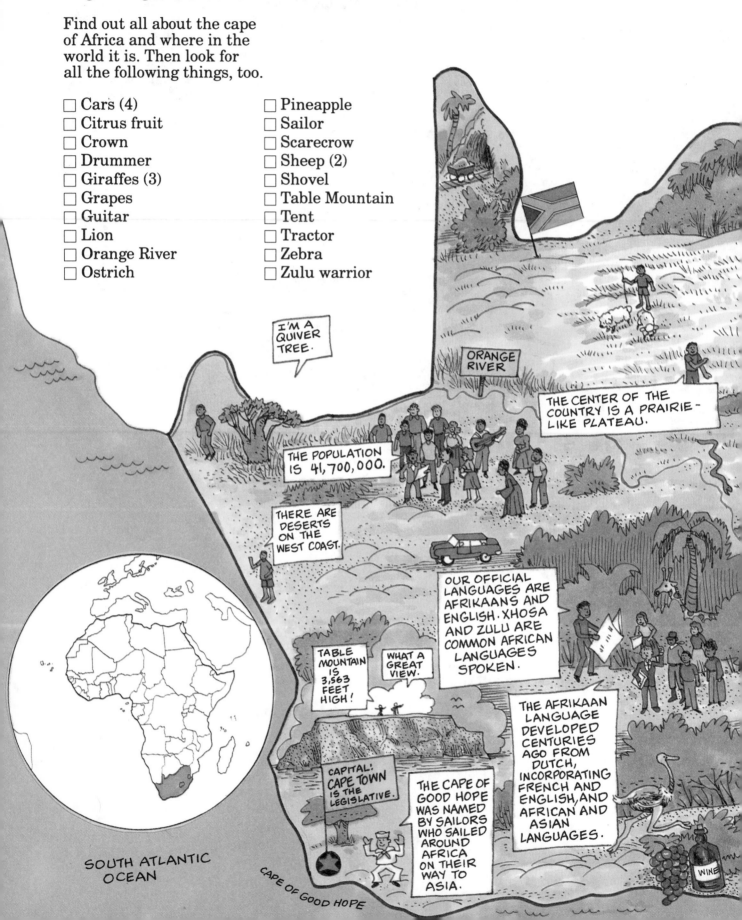

I'M A QUIVER TREE.

ORANGE RIVER

THE CENTER OF THE COUNTRY IS A PRAIRIE-LIKE PLATEAU.

THE POPULATION IS 41,700,000.

THERE ARE DESERTS ON THE WEST COAST.

TABLE MOUNTAIN IS 3,563 FEET HIGH!

WHAT A GREAT VIEW.

OUR OFFICIAL LANGUAGES ARE AFRIKAANS AND ENGLISH. XHOSA AND ZULU ARE COMMON AFRICAN LANGUAGES SPOKEN.

THE AFRIKAAN LANGUAGE DEVELOPED CENTURIES AGO FROM DUTCH, INCORPORATING FRENCH AND ENGLISH, AND AFRICAN AND ASIAN LANGUAGES.

CAPITAL: CAPE TOWN IS THE LEGISLATIVE.

THE CAPE OF GOOD HOPE WAS NAMED BY SAILORS WHO SAILED AROUND AFRICA ON THEIR WAY TO ASIA.

SOUTH ATLANTIC OCEAN

CAPE OF GOOD HOPE

WINE

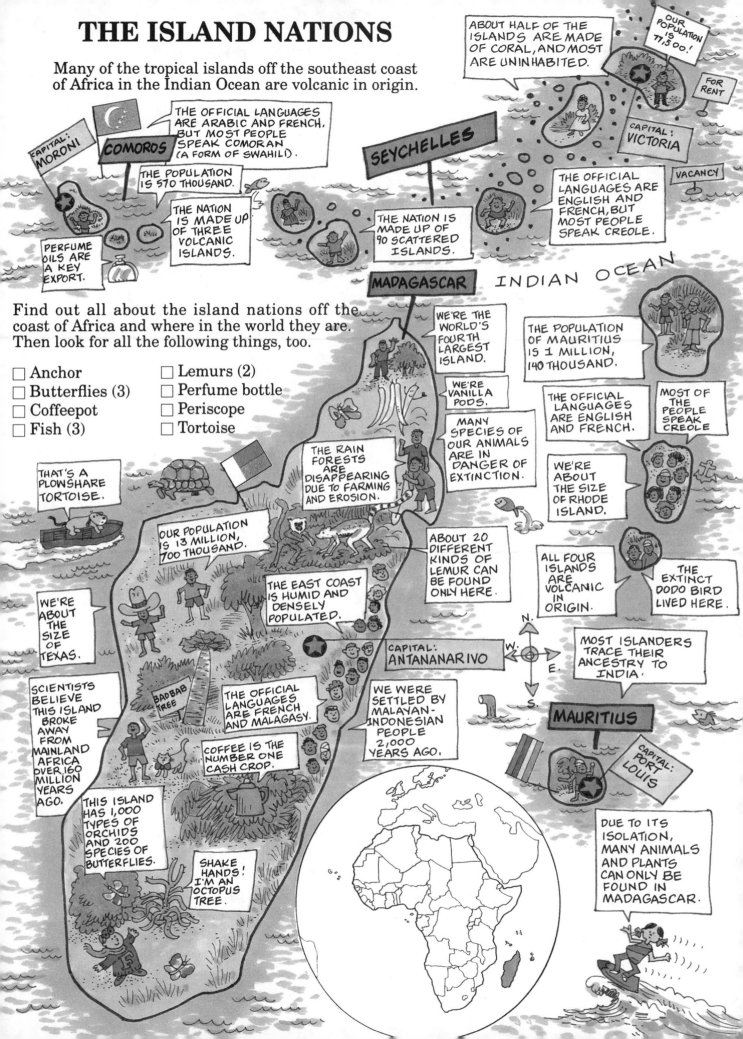

NORTH AND SOUTH AMERICA

IV

Search and find lots of interesting facts about:

- Mexico and Central America

- The Caribbean Islands

- The Northern Coast of South America

- Central South America

- Southern South America

- The U.S.: The Northeast

- The U.S.: The Southern States

- The U.S.: The Midwest

- The U.S.: The Western States

- Eastern Canada and Greenland

- Central and Western Canada

- Alaska

NORTH AND SOUTH AMERICA

ARCTIC OCEAN

BEAUFORT SEA

ICELAND

GREENLAND

BAFFIN BAY

LABRADOR SEA

HUDSON BAY

GREAT BEAR LAKE

GREAT SLAVE LAKE

LAKE WINNIPEG

MACKENZIE RIVER

MACKENZIE MTS.

MT. LOGAN

CANADA IS 3,851,817 SQUARE MILES.

CANADA'S POPULATION IS ABOUT 29 MILLION.

THAT'S THE HIGHEST MOUNTAIN IN NORTH AMERICA.

ALASKA

MT. MCKINLEY

GULF OF ALASKA

LAKE SUPERIOR

LAKE HURON

LAKE MICHIGAN

LAKE ONTARIO

LAKE ERIE

CANADA

UNITED STATES

ROCKY MOUNTAINS

MISSOURI RIVER

GRAND CANYON

SIERRA NEVEDA MTS.

APPALACHIAN MTS.

MISSISSIPPI RIVER

RIO GRANDE RIVER

MEXICO

SIERRA MADRE MTS.

THE POPULATION OF THE U.S. IS ABOUT 265 MILLION.

MEXICO'S POPULATION IS ABOUT 96 MILLION.

I'M A RACCOON, AND YOU'RE NOT.

I'M A SWORDFISH.

THE U.S. COVERS 3,618,794 SQUARE MILES.

BUT THAT'S MOSTLY LAND!

WHAT GOOD IS LAND?

NORTH

EAST

WEST

SOUTH

AFRICA

SOUTH AMERICA IS THE FOURTH LARGEST CONTINENT AFTER ASIA, AFRICA AND NORTH AMERICA.

ATLANTIC OCEAN

BERMUDA

GULF OF MEXICO

PACIFIC OCEAN

GUATEMALA

EL SALVADOR

COSTA RICA

BELIZE

HONDURAS

NICARAGUA

PANAMA

JAMAICA

CUBA

HAITI

DOMINICAN REPUBLIC

PUERTO RICO

LESSER ANTILLES

GREATER ANTILLES

CARIBBEAN SEA

COLUMBIA

VENEZUELA

GUYANA

SURINAME

FRENCH GUIANA

EQUATOR

EQUATOR

THE POPULATION OF SOUTH AMERICA IS ABOUT 325 MILLION.

HOW DID THAT FISH KNOW THAT?

SOUTH AMERICA COVERS 6,886,000 SQUARE MILES.

I'VE HEARD OF THAT!

A GAUCHO IS A CATTLEHERDER.

THE STRONG WIND AND CURRENTS AROUND CAPE HORN HAVE MADE IT A GRAVE YARD FOR SHIPS.

THE MAIN LANGUAGE IN CENTRAL AND SOUTH AMERICA IS SPANISH—EXCEPT FOR BRAZIL, WHERE PORTUGUESE IS SPOKEN.

THE ANDES MT. RANGE IS THE LONGEST RANGE IN THE WORLD.

AMAZON RIVER

BRAZIL

PARAGUAY

URUGUAY

ANDES MTS.

BOLIVIA

ARGENTINA

ANDES MTS.

CAPE HORN

ATACAMA DESERT

CHILE

PERU

ECUADOR

MUCH OF SOUTH AMERICA IS BELOW THE EQUATOR, WHICH MEANS THAT SUMMER IS IN JANUARY, AND WINTER IN AUGUST.

ANTARCTIC CIRCLE

The continents of North and South America were developing for thousands of years before Europeans arrived. When explorers and settlers did come from across the sea, starting in the late 15th century, native civilizations and the land were greatly changed.

Find out all about North and South America, and where in the world they are. Then look for all the following things, too.

- ☐ Banana
- ☐ Cactuses (2)
- ☐ Coffeepot
- ☐ Igloo
- ☐ Monkey
- ☐ Moose
- ☐ Penguin
- ☐ Periscope
- ☐ Ruler
- ☐ Sailboats (2)
- ☐ Shipwreck
- ☐ Soccer player
- ☐ Surfer
- ☐ Swordfish

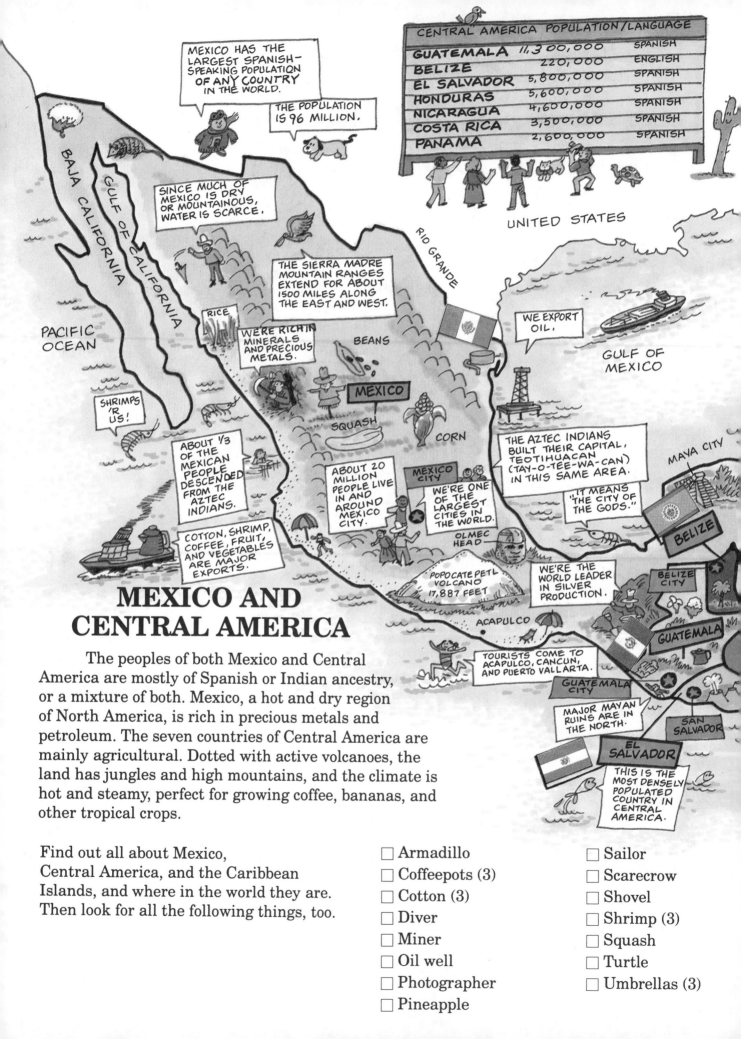

MEXICO AND CENTRAL AMERICA

The peoples of both Mexico and Central America are mostly of Spanish or Indian ancestry, or a mixture of both. Mexico, a hot and dry region of North America, is rich in precious metals and petroleum. The seven countries of Central America are mainly agricultural. Dotted with active volcanoes, the land has jungles and high mountains, and the climate is hot and steamy, perfect for growing coffee, bananas, and other tropical crops.

Find out all about Mexico, Central America, and the Caribbean Islands, and where in the world they are. Then look for all the following things, too.

- ☐ Armadillo
- ☐ Coffeepots (3)
- ☐ Cotton (3)
- ☐ Diver
- ☐ Miner
- ☐ Oil well
- ☐ Photographer
- ☐ Pineapple
- ☐ Sailor
- ☐ Scarecrow
- ☐ Shovel
- ☐ Shrimp (3)
- ☐ Squash
- ☐ Turtle
- ☐ Umbrellas (3)

THE CARIBBEAN ISLANDS

In the Caribbean Sea lies a chain of tropical islands that stretch for 2,000 miles down to the coast of South America. The islands were colonized in the 16th century by Europeans, who brought over African slaves to work plantations. Today, these islands form 25 separate countries. The islanders, most of whom are descendants of slaves, mainly depend on tourism and agriculture for their income.

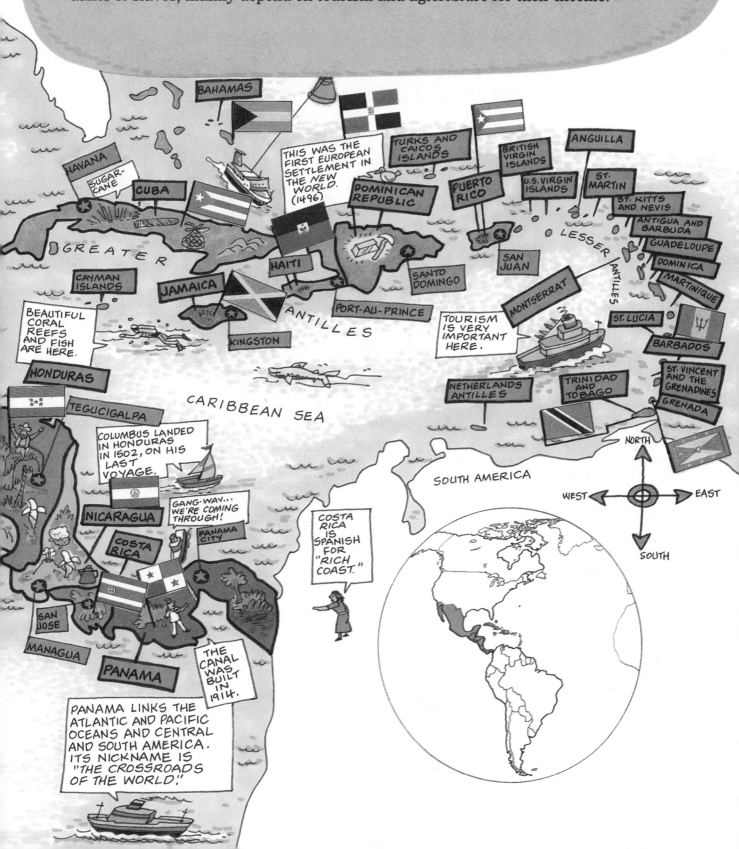

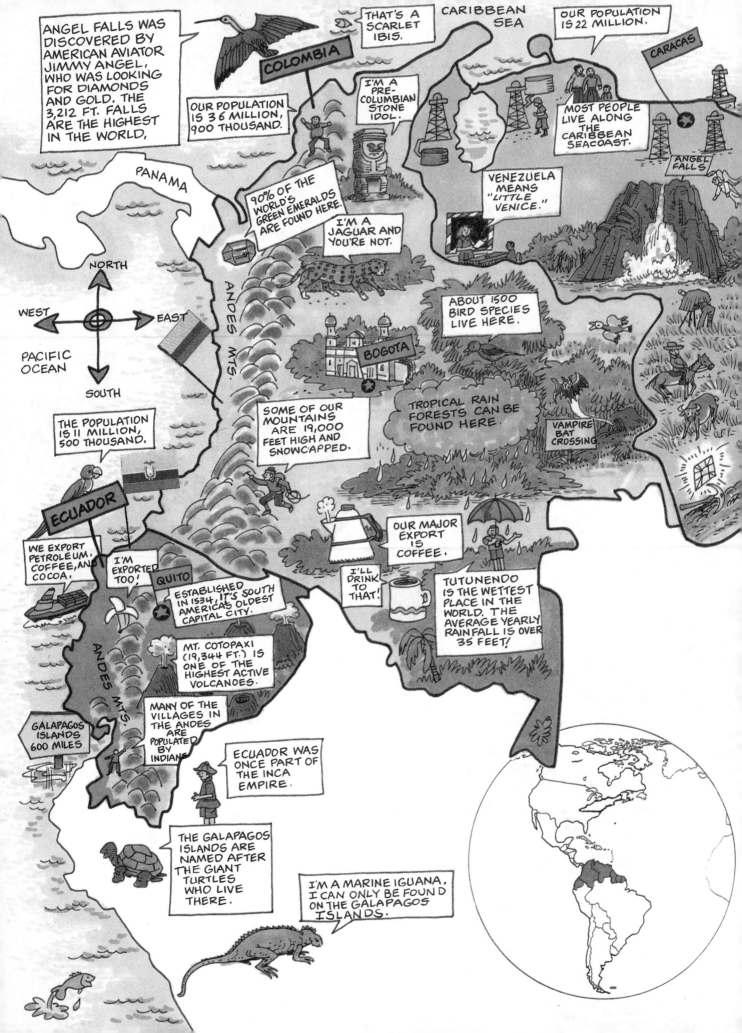

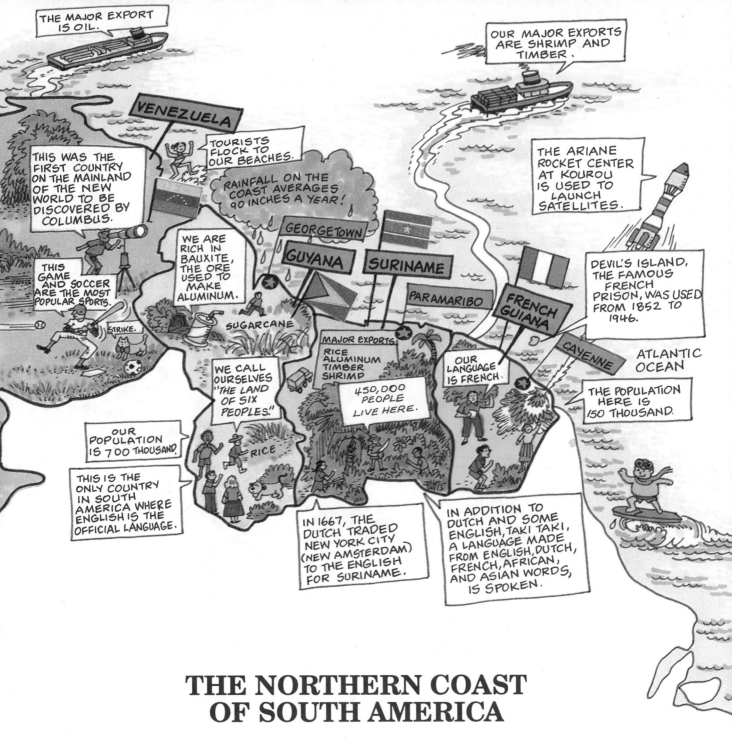

THE NORTHERN COAST OF SOUTH AMERICA

The northern part of South America is dominated by the Andes Mountains in the west, and by the Amazon forest. The people, like the rest of South America, are of European, Indian, and mixed ancestry.

Find out all about the countries along the northern coast of South America, and where in the world they are. Then look for all the following things, too.

- ☐ Angel
- ☐ Baseball bat
- ☐ Bat
- ☐ Can
- ☐ Cup
- ☐ Emerald
- ☐ Ibis
- ☐ Iguana
- ☐ Jaguar
- ☐ Mountain climber
- ☐ Photographer
- ☐ Satellite rocket
- ☐ Schoolteacher
- ☐ Stone idol
- ☐ Surfer
- ☐ Telescope
- ☐ Turtle

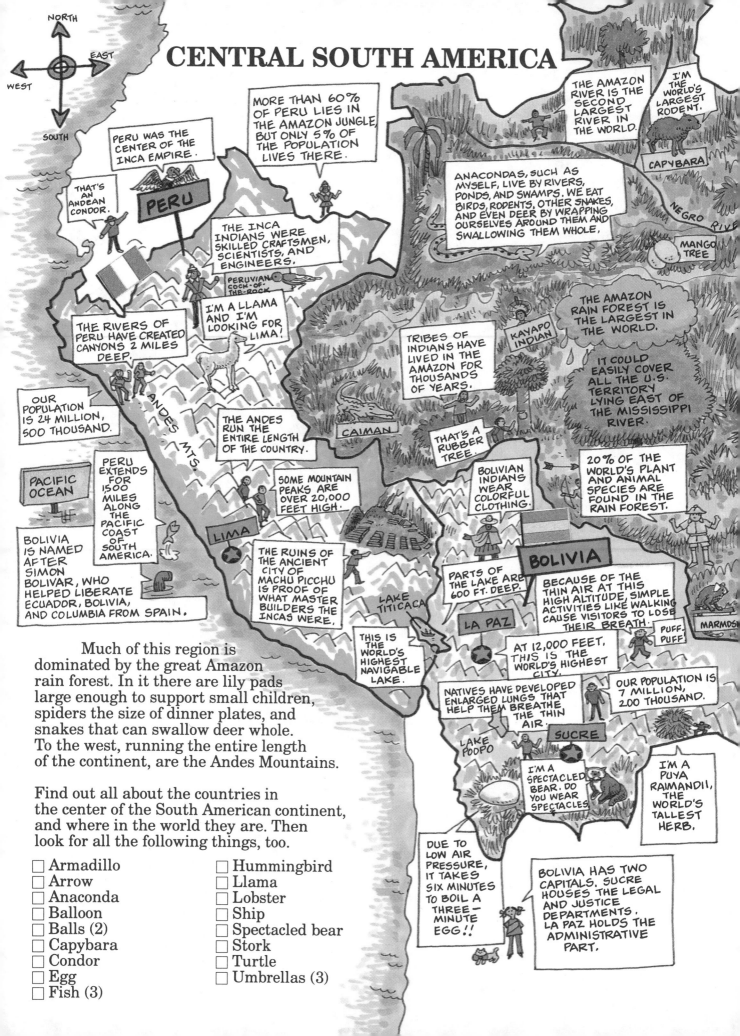

CENTRAL SOUTH AMERICA

THE AMAZON RIVER IS THE SECOND LARGEST RIVER IN THE WORLD.

I'M THE WORLD'S LARGEST RODENT.

MORE THAN 60% OF PERU LIES IN THE AMAZON JUNGLE, BUT ONLY 5% OF THE POPULATION LIVES THERE.

PERU WAS THE CENTER OF THE INCA EMPIRE.

THAT'S AN ANDEAN CONDOR.

CAPYBARA

ANACONDAS, SUCH AS MYSELF, LIVE BY RIVERS, PONDS, AND SWAMPS. WE EAT BIRDS, RODENTS, OTHER SNAKES, AND EVEN DEER BY WRAPPING OURSELVES AROUND THEM AND SWALLOWING THEM WHOLE.

NEGRO RIVER

PERU

THE INCA INDIANS WERE SKILLED CRAFTSMEN, SCIENTISTS, AND ENGINEERS.

PERUVIAN COCK-OF-THE-ROCK

MANGO TREE

I'M A LLAMA AND I'M LOOKING FOR LIMA!

THE RIVERS OF PERU HAVE CREATED CANYONS 2 MILES DEEP.

TRIBES OF INDIANS HAVE LIVED IN THE AMAZON FOR THOUSANDS OF YEARS.

KAYAPO INDIAN

THE AMAZON RAIN FOREST IS THE LARGEST IN THE WORLD.

IT COULD EASILY COVER ALL THE U.S. TERRITORY LYING EAST OF THE MISSISSIPPI RIVER.

OUR POPULATION IS 24 MILLION, 500 THOUSAND.

THE ANDES RUN THE ENTIRE LENGTH OF THE COUNTRY.

ANDES MTS.

CAIMAN

THAT'S A RUBBER TREE.

BOLIVIAN INDIANS WEAR COLORFUL CLOTHING.

20% OF THE WORLD'S PLANT AND ANIMAL SPECIES ARE FOUND IN THE RAIN FOREST.

PACIFIC OCEAN

PERU EXTENDS FOR 1500 MILES ALONG THE PACIFIC COAST OF SOUTH AMERICA.

SOME MOUNTAIN PEAKS ARE OVER 20,000 FEET HIGH.

LIMA

BOLIVIA IS NAMED AFTER SIMON BOLIVAR, WHO HELPED LIBERATE ECUADOR, BOLIVIA, AND COLUMBIA FROM SPAIN.

THE RUINS OF THE ANCIENT CITY OF MACHU PICCHU IS PROOF OF WHAT MASTER BUILDERS THE INCAS WERE.

BOLIVIA

PARTS OF THE LAKE ARE 600 FT. DEEP.

BECAUSE OF THE THIN AIR AT THIS HIGH ALTITUDE, SIMPLE ACTIVITIES LIKE WALKING CAUSE VISITORS TO LOSE THEIR BREATH.

PUFF, PUFF!

MARMOSET

LAKE TITICACA

THIS IS THE WORLD'S HIGHEST NAVIGABLE LAKE.

LA PAZ

AT 12,000 FEET, THIS IS THE WORLD'S HIGHEST CITY.

Much of this region is dominated by the great Amazon rain forest. In it there are lily pads large enough to support small children, spiders the size of dinner plates, and snakes that can swallow deer whole. To the west, running the entire length of the continent, are the Andes Mountains.

NATIVES HAVE DEVELOPED ENLARGED LUNGS THAT HELP THEM BREATHE THE THIN AIR.

OUR POPULATION IS 7 MILLION, 200 THOUSAND.

LAKE POOPO

SUCRE

I'M A SPECTACLED BEAR. DO YOU WEAR SPECTACLES?

I'M A PUYA RAIMANDII, THE WORLD'S TALLEST HERB.

Find out all about the countries in the center of the South American continent, and where in the world they are. Then look for all the following things, too.

DUE TO LOW AIR PRESSURE, IT TAKES SIX MINUTES TO BOIL A THREE-MINUTE EGG!!

BOLIVIA HAS TWO CAPITALS. SUCRE HOUSES THE LEGAL AND JUSTICE DEPARTMENTS. LA PAZ HOLDS THE ADMINISTRATIVE PART.

- ☐ Armadillo
- ☐ Arrow
- ☐ Anaconda
- ☐ Balloon
- ☐ Balls (2)
- ☐ Capybara
- ☐ Condor
- ☐ Egg
- ☐ Fish (3)
- ☐ Hummingbird
- ☐ Llama
- ☐ Lobster
- ☐ Ship
- ☐ Spectacled bear
- ☐ Stork
- ☐ Turtle
- ☐ Umbrellas (3)

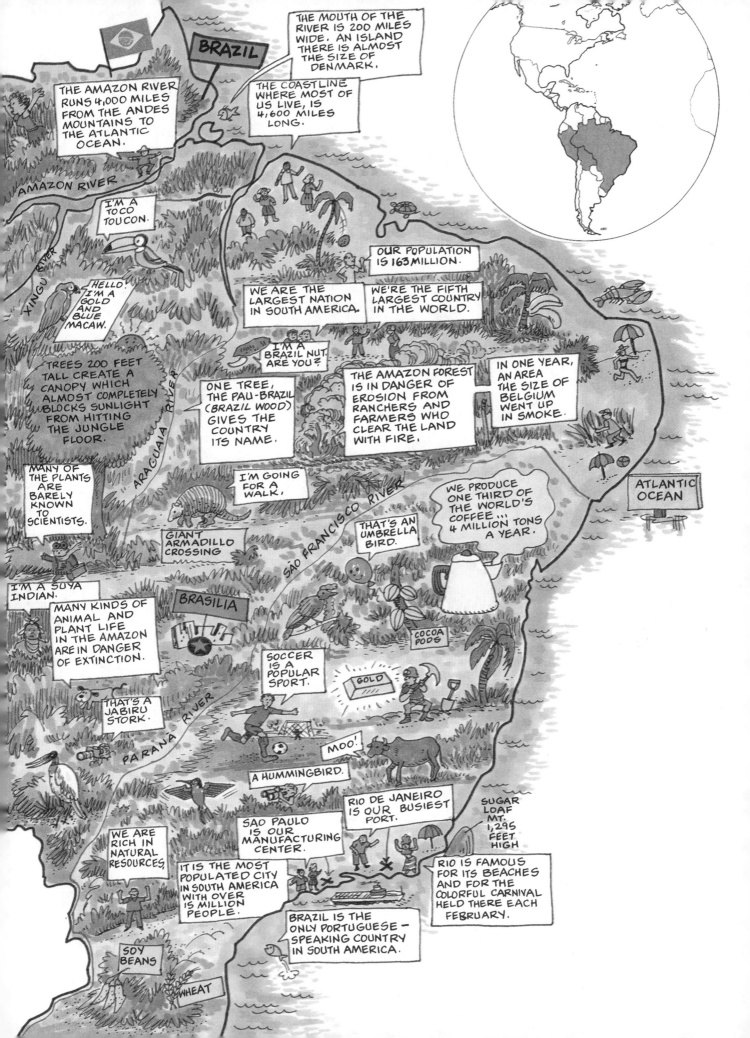

SOUTHERN SOUTH AMERICA

The southern region of South America has various types of landscapes, including grassy plains, deserts, mountains, forests, and frozen glaciers. It is a region rich in natural resources.

Find out all about the countries in the southern part of South America, and where in the world they are. Then look for all the following things, too.

- ☐ Albatross
- ☐ Anteater
- ☐ Ball
- ☐ Boat
- ☐ Dancers
- ☐ Grapes
- ☐ Hairy armadillo
- ☐ Heart

NORTH
EAST
SOUTH
WEST

PACIFIC OCEAN

CHILE

CHILE EXTENDS ALONG THE WESTERN COAST OF S.A. FOR 2,650 MILES, ABOUT THE DISTANCE FROM NEW YORK TO SAN FRANCISCO.

IN SOME PLACES IT'S AS NARROW AS 15 MILES ACROSS.

RAIN FELL IN THE ATACAMA DESERT IN 1971 FOR THE FIRST TIME IN 400 YEARS.

IT'S A LONG WAIT.

THAT'S A CONDOR.

MT. ACONCAGUA (22,834 FT.) IS THE HIGHEST PEAK IN THE WORLD OUTSIDE OF THOSE IN ASIA.

ATACAMA DESERT

THE DESERT IS VERY DRY, BUT VERY RICH IN COPPER, GOLD, AND SILVER.

OUR POPULATION IS 14 MILLION, 400 THOUSAND.

LICANCABUR VOLCANO (19,425 FT.)

ARGENTINA

THE ANDES MOUNTAINS RUN LIKE A SPINE DOWN THE CHILE-ARGENTINE BORDER.

I'M A GIANT ANTEATER.

I HAVEN'T SEEN ANY GIANT ANTS!

MT. OJOS DEL SALADO (22,660 FT.) IS THE WORLD'S HIGHEST ACTIVE VOLCANO.

ARGENTINA IS THE SECOND-LARGEST COUNTRY IN S.A. IT IS ABOUT ONE-THIRD THE SIZE OF THE U.S.

OUR POPULATION IS 34,700,000.

POLO IS POPULAR HERE.

SANTIAGO

WINE MAKING IS A MAJOR INDUSTRY.

CHERRIES

SUGARCANE

ANDES MOUNTAINS

THIS IS A FERTILE GRASSY PLAIN WHERE CATTLE ARE RAISED.

PAMPAS

95% OF THE POPULATION IS OF EUROPEAN ANCESTRY.

BUENOS AIRES

PARAGUAY

MOST PARAGUAYANS ARE PART GUARANI INDIAN AND PART SPANISH. BOTH LANGUAGES ARE SPOKEN.

THE WEST IS A DRY GRASSLAND WHERE CATTLE GRAZE ON LARGE RANCHES.

I'M A GAUCHO.

THAT'S A CATTLE HERDER.

THE QUEBRACHO TREE, CALLED THE "AXE BREAKER," IS SO DENSE AND HEAVY THAT THE WOOD SINKS IN WATER.

OUR POPULATION IS 5 MILLION, 500 THOUSAND.

THE PARANA RIVER DIVIDES THIS LANDLOCKED COUNTRY.

IQUASSI FALLS ON THE PARANA RIVER IS A SPECTACULAR SIGHT.

ORANGES

ASUNCION

THE EAST PRODUCES SOYBEANS, COFFEE, RICE, AND TROPICAL FRUIT.

COTTON

URUGUAY RIVER

URUGUAY

OUR POPULATION IS 3 MILLION, 300 THOUSAND.

WOULD YOU LIKE A CUP OF MATE?

IT'S A TYPE OF TEA.

IN SPRING, A PURPLE FLOWER BLOOMS, GIVING US THE NICKNAME OF "THE PURPLE LAND."

MONTEVIDEO

PARANA RIVER

BEAUTIFUL BEACHES

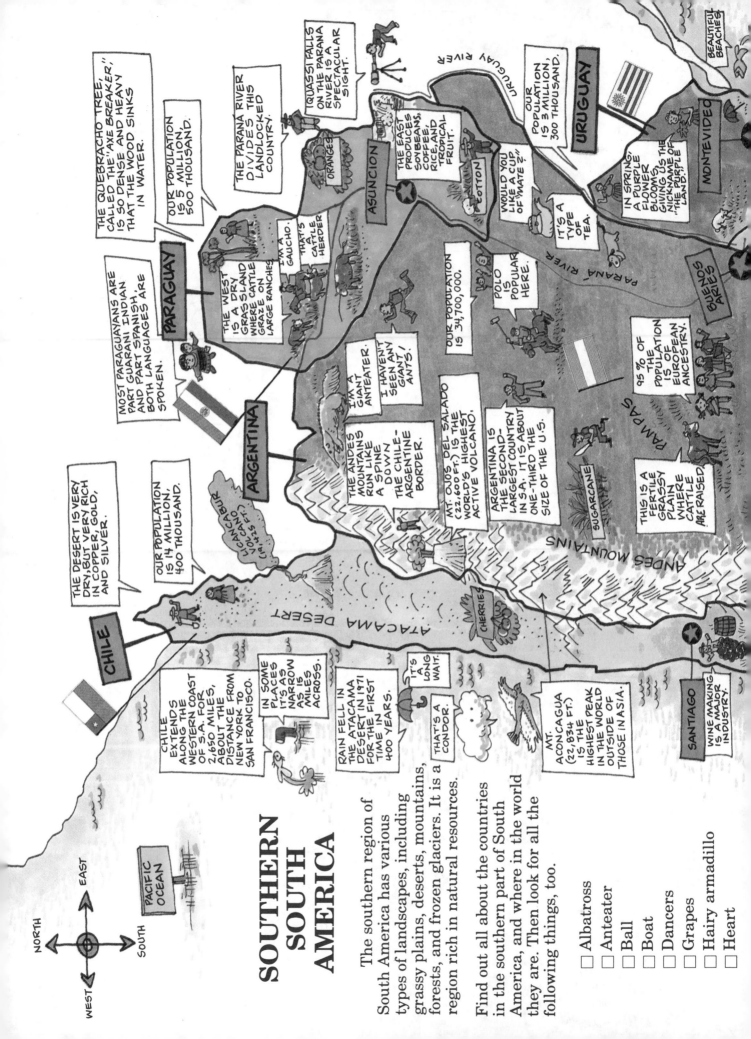

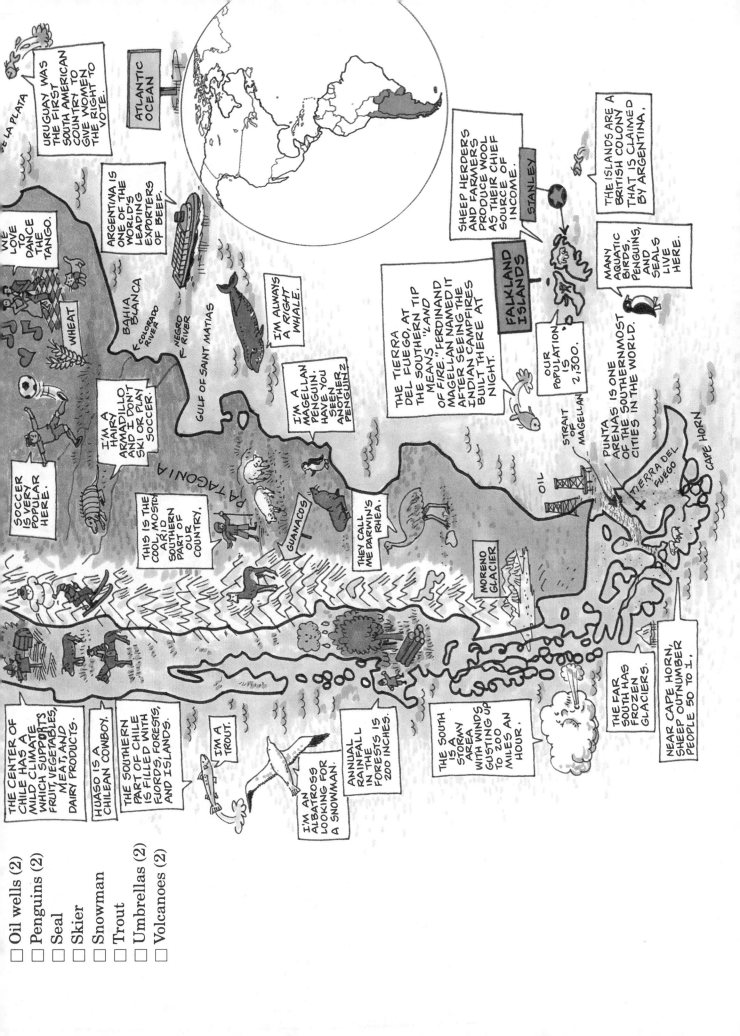

Oil wells (2)
Penguins (2)
Seal
Skier
Snowman
Trout
Umbrellas (2)
Volcanoes (2)

THE UNITED STATES
The Northeast

The most populous region in the country, the northeast was the first to be settled by Europeans. Colonists arrived from England in 1620 and settled New Plymouth, Massachusetts.

Find out all about the northeastern states, and where in the world they are. Then look for all the following things, too.

☐ Anchor
☐ Apple
☐ Baseball
☐ Basketball
☐ Cannon
☐ Kite
☐ Lighthouse
☐ Lobster
☐ Ship
☐ Skier
☐ Treasure chest
☐ Truck
☐ Umbrella

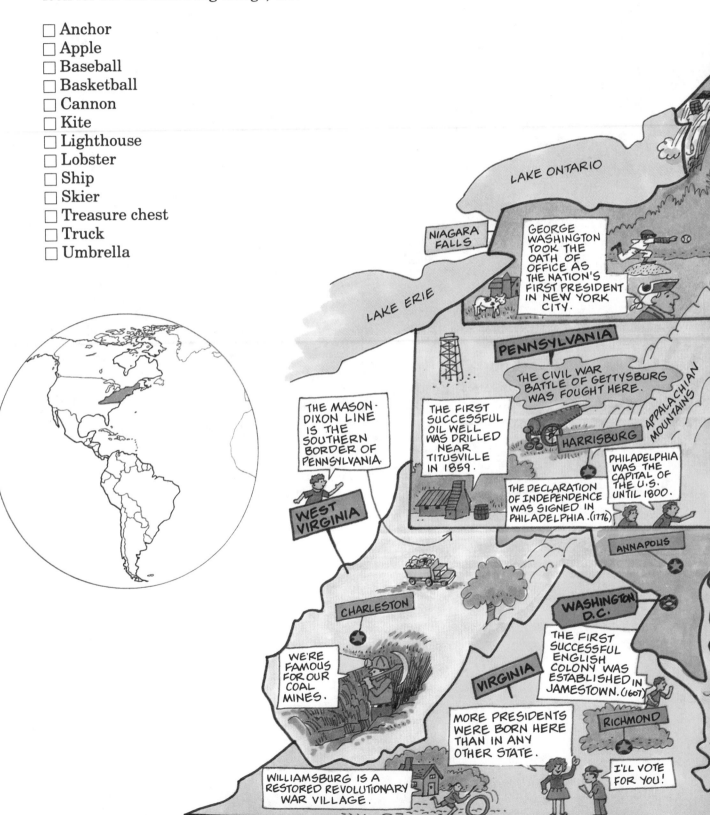

LAKE ONTARIO

NIAGARA FALLS

GEORGE WASHINGTON TOOK THE OATH OF OFFICE AS THE NATION'S FIRST PRESIDENT IN NEW YORK CITY.

LAKE ERIE

PENNSYLVANIA

THE CIVIL WAR BATTLE OF GETTYSBURG WAS FOUGHT HERE.

APPALACHIAN MOUNTAINS

THE MASON-DIXON LINE IS THE SOUTHERN BORDER OF PENNSYLVANIA.

THE FIRST SUCCESSFUL OIL WELL WAS DRILLED NEAR TITUSVILLE IN 1859.

HARRISBURG

PHILADELPHIA WAS THE CAPITAL OF THE U.S. UNTIL 1800.

THE DECLARATION OF INDEPENDENCE WAS SIGNED IN PHILADELPHIA. (1776)

WEST VIRGINIA

ANNAPOLIS

CHARLESTON

WASHINGTON D.C.

THE FIRST SUCCESSFUL ENGLISH COLONY WAS ESTABLISHED IN JAMESTOWN. (1607)

WE'RE FAMOUS FOR OUR COAL MINES.

VIRGINIA

RICHMOND

MORE PRESIDENTS WERE BORN HERE THAN IN ANY OTHER STATE.

I'LL VOTE FOR YOU!

WILLIAMSBURG IS A RESTORED REVOLUTIONARY WAR VILLAGE.

The Southern States

The southern states, which extend from the Atlanti coast to Texas, were once totally farm based, producing mainly cotton and tobacco. Although still agricultural, the area is now strong in industry, and produces oil as well as iron and steel.

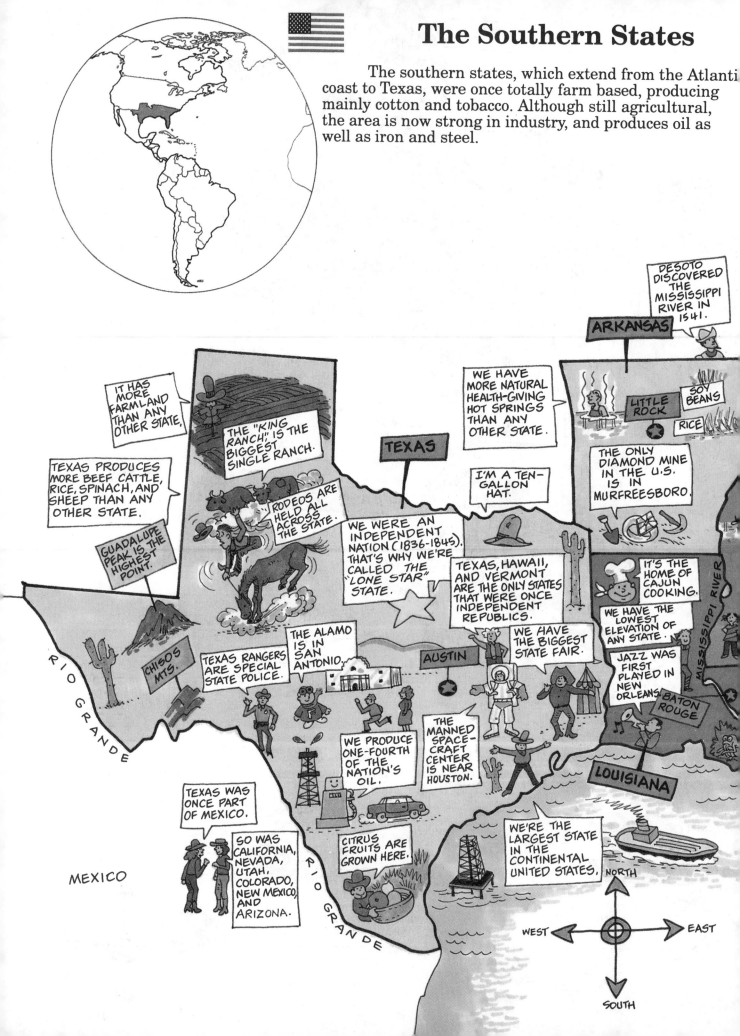

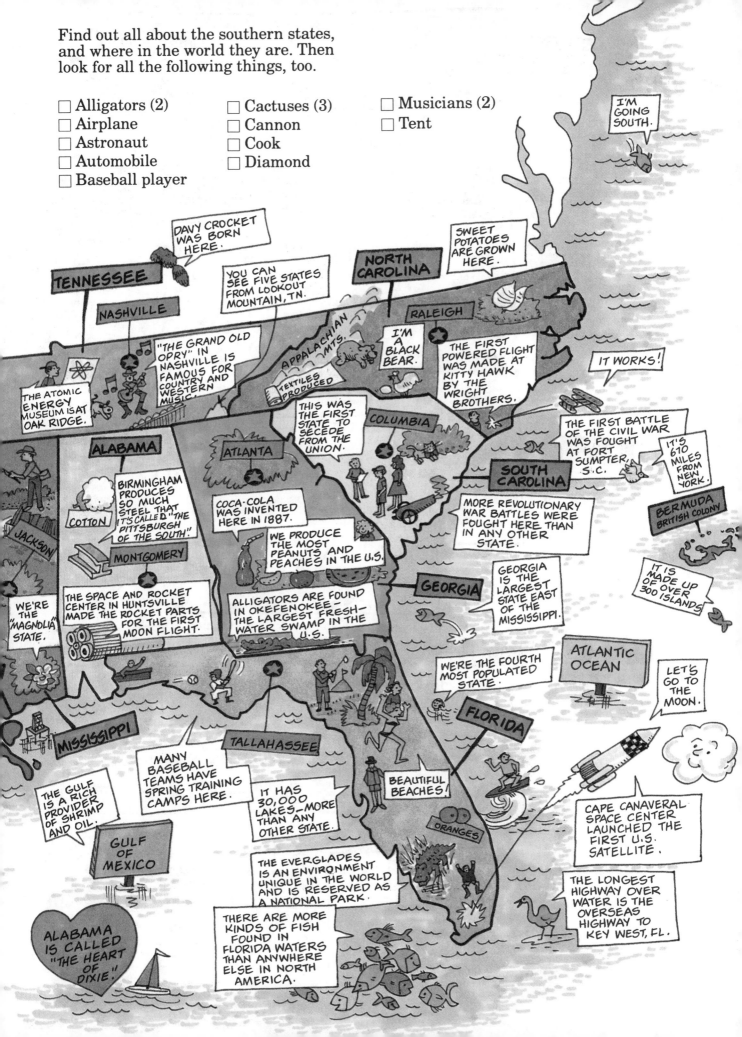

Find out all about the southern states, and where in the world they are. Then look for all the following things, too.

- ☐ Alligators (2)
- ☐ Airplane
- ☐ Astronaut
- ☐ Automobile
- ☐ Baseball player
- ☐ Cactuses (3)
- ☐ Cannon
- ☐ Cook
- ☐ Diamond
- ☐ Musicians (2)
- ☐ Tent

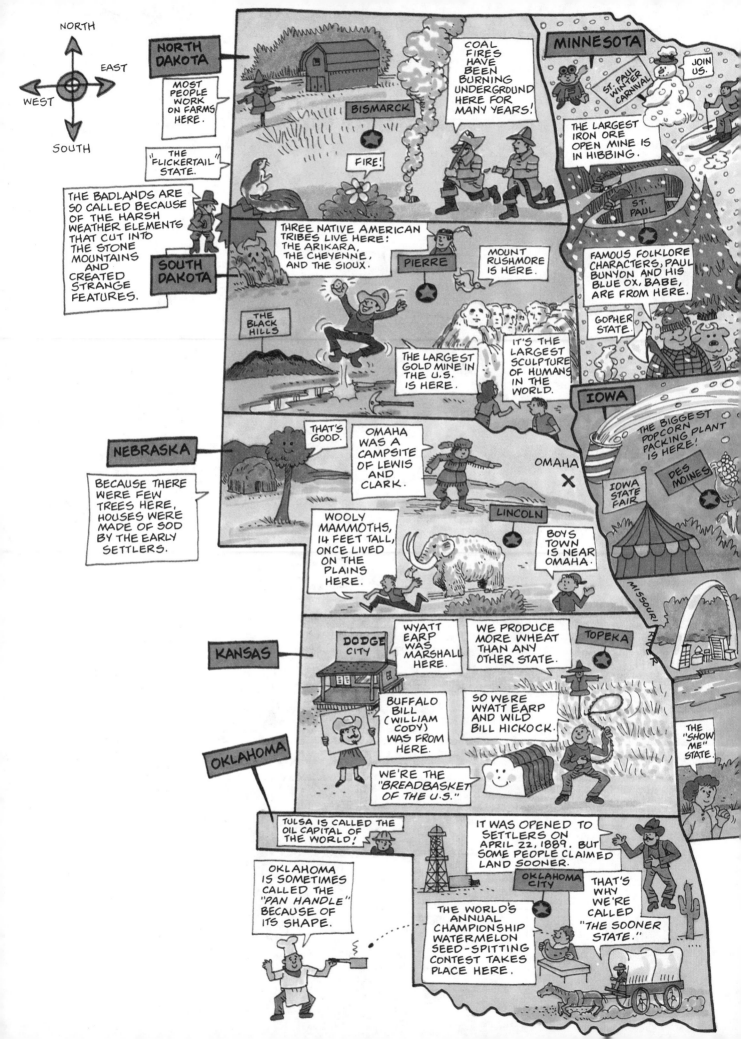

The Midwest

Between the Great Lakes in the north, the Rocky Mountains in the west, and the Appalachians in the east, lies the flat and fertile area known as the Great Plains. The area produces more than half of the world's corn and enough wheat to make the United States the world's largest exporter.

Find out all about the midwestern states, and where in the world they are. Then look for all the following things, too.

- [ ] Blue ox
- [ ] Book
- [ ] Cereal
- [ ] Flower
- [ ] Football
- [ ] Heart
- [ ] Race cars (3)
- [ ] Santa Claus
- [ ] Snowman
- [ ] Tire
- [ ] Watermelon slice
- [ ] Wooly mammoth

The Western States

The western part of the United States is characterized by deserts, mountains, river canyons, and great forests. Separated from the east by the Rocky Mountains, the area was greatly settled and developed mostly after the mid 1880's when the railroads linked the west to the east.

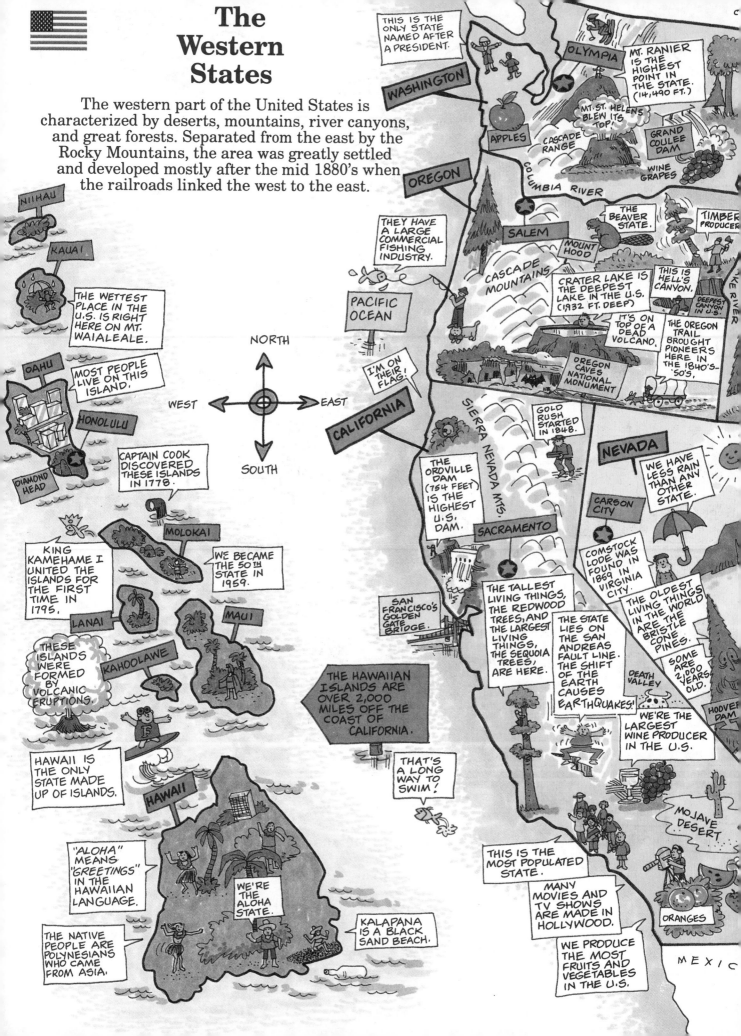

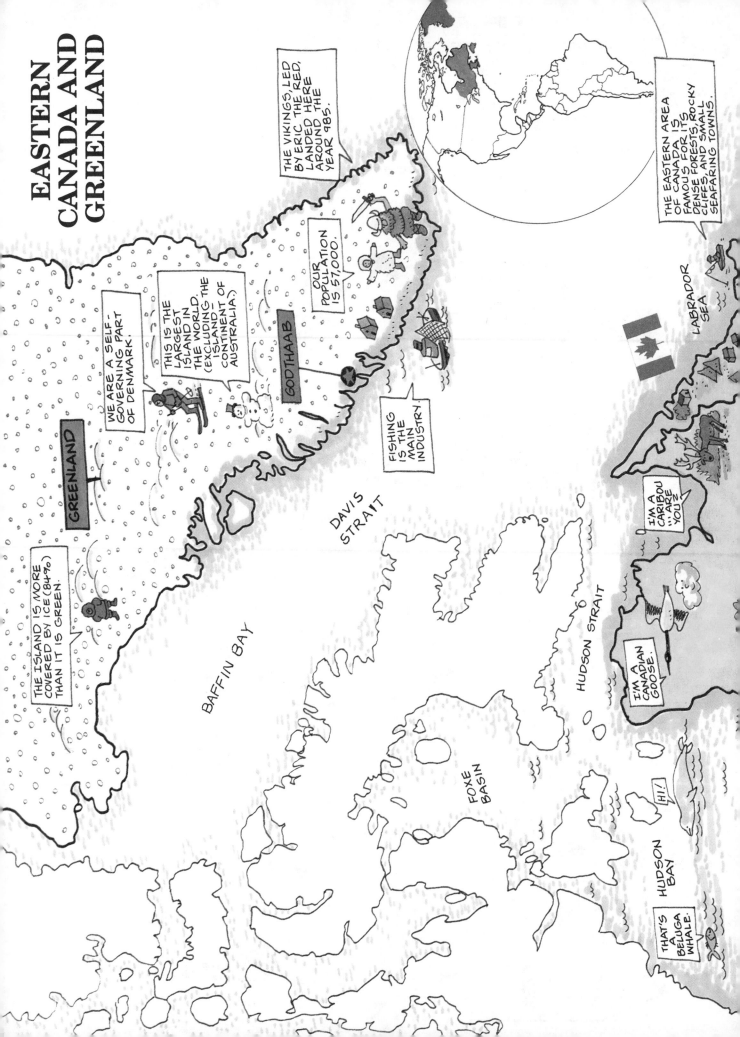

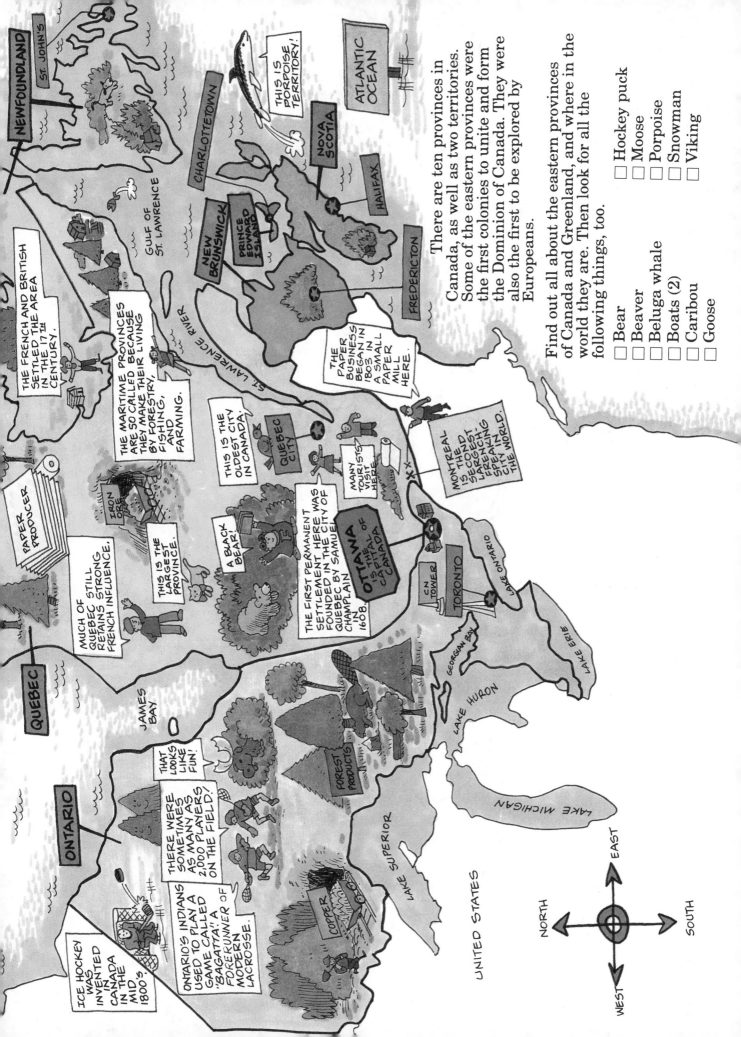

There are ten provinces in Canada, as well as two territories. Some of the first colonies were the first provinces to unite and form the Dominion of Canada. They were also the first to be explored by Europeans.

Find out all about the eastern provinces of Canada and Greenland, and where in the world they are. Then look for all the following things, too.

☐ Bear
☐ Beaver
☐ Beluga whale
☐ Boats (2)
☐ Caribou
☐ Goose
☐ Hockey puck
☐ Moose
☐ Porpoise
☐ Snowman
☐ Viking

NEWFOUNDLAND
ST. JOHN'S

THIS IS PORPOISE TERRITORY!

CHARLOTTETOWN

NOVA SCOTIA

HALIFAX

ATLANTIC OCEAN

NEW BRUNSWICK

PRINCE EDWARD ISLAND

FREDERICTON

THE PAPER BUSINESS BEGAN IN 1803 IN A SMALL PAPER MILL HERE.

GULF OF ST. LAWRENCE

THE FRENCH AND BRITISH SETTLED THE AREA IN THE 17TH CENTURY.

THE MARITIME PROVINCES ARE SO CALLED BECAUSE THEY MAKE THEIR LIVING BY FORESTRY, FISHING, AND FARMING.

ST. LAWRENCE RIVER

THIS IS THE OLDEST CITY IN CANADA.

QUEBEC CITY

MANY TOURISTS VISIT HERE.

MONTREAL IS THE SECOND LARGEST FRENCH SPEAKING CITY IN THE WORLD.

PAPER PRODUCER

IRON ORE

THIS IS THE LARGEST PROVINCE.

MUCH OF QUEBEC STILL RETAINS STRONG FRENCH INFLUENCE.

A BLACK BEAR!

THE FIRST PERMANENT SETTLEMENT HERE WAS FOUNDED IN THE CITY OF QUEBEC BY SAMUEL CHAMPLAIN IN 1608.

OTTAWA IS THE CAPITAL OF CANADA

CN TOWER

TORONTO

LAKE ONTARIO

QUEBEC

JAMES BAY

THAT LOOKS LIKE FUN!

GEORGIAN BAY

LAKE HURON

LAKE ERIE

LAKE MICHIGAN

ONTARIO

FOREST PRODUCTS

LAKE SUPERIOR

THERE WERE SOMETIMES AS MANY AS 2,000 PLAYERS ON THE FIELD!

ONTARIO'S INDIANS USED TO PLAY A GAME CALLED "BAGATTA," A FORERUNNER OF MODERN LACROSSE.

ICE HOCKEY WAS INVENTED IN CANADA IN THE MID 1800'S.

COPPER

UNITED STATES

NORTH
EAST
SOUTH
WEST

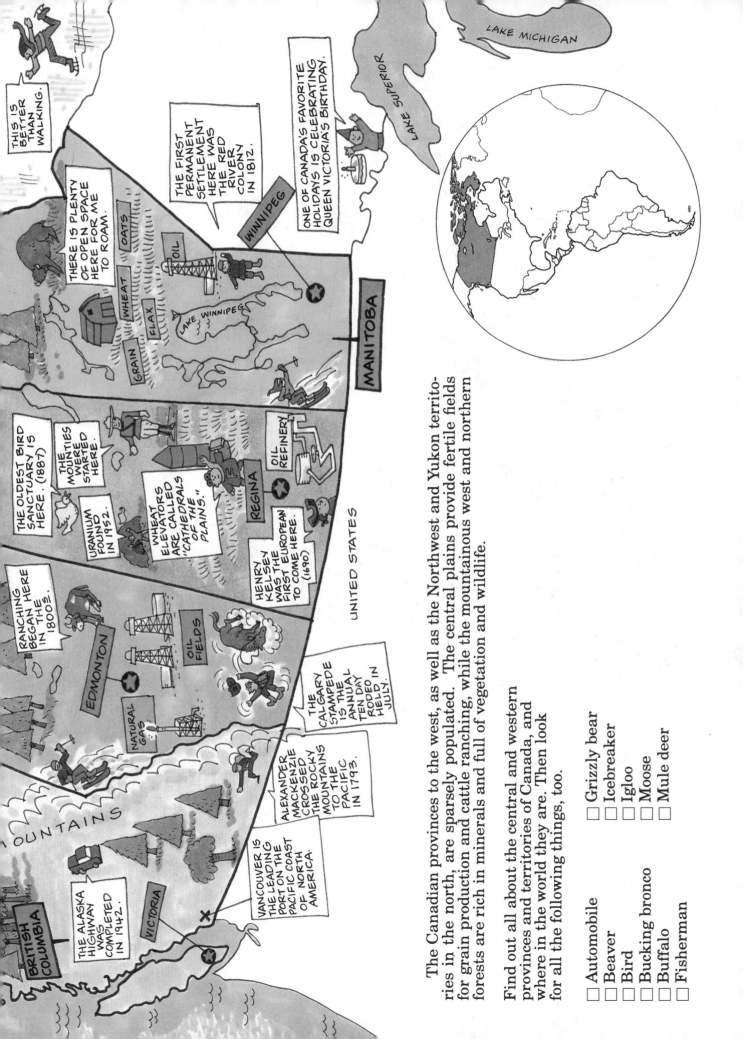

The Canadian provinces to the west, as well as the Northwest and Yukon territories in the north, are sparsely populated. The central plains provide fertile fields for grain production and cattle ranching, while the mountainous west and northern forests are rich in minerals and full of vegetation and wildlife.

Find out all about the central and western provinces and territories of Canada, and where in the world they are. Then look for all the following things, too.

☐ Automobile
☐ Beaver
☐ Bird
☐ Bucking bronco
☐ Buffalo
☐ Fisherman
☐ Grizzly bear
☐ Icebreaker
☐ Igloo
☐ Moose
☐ Mule deer

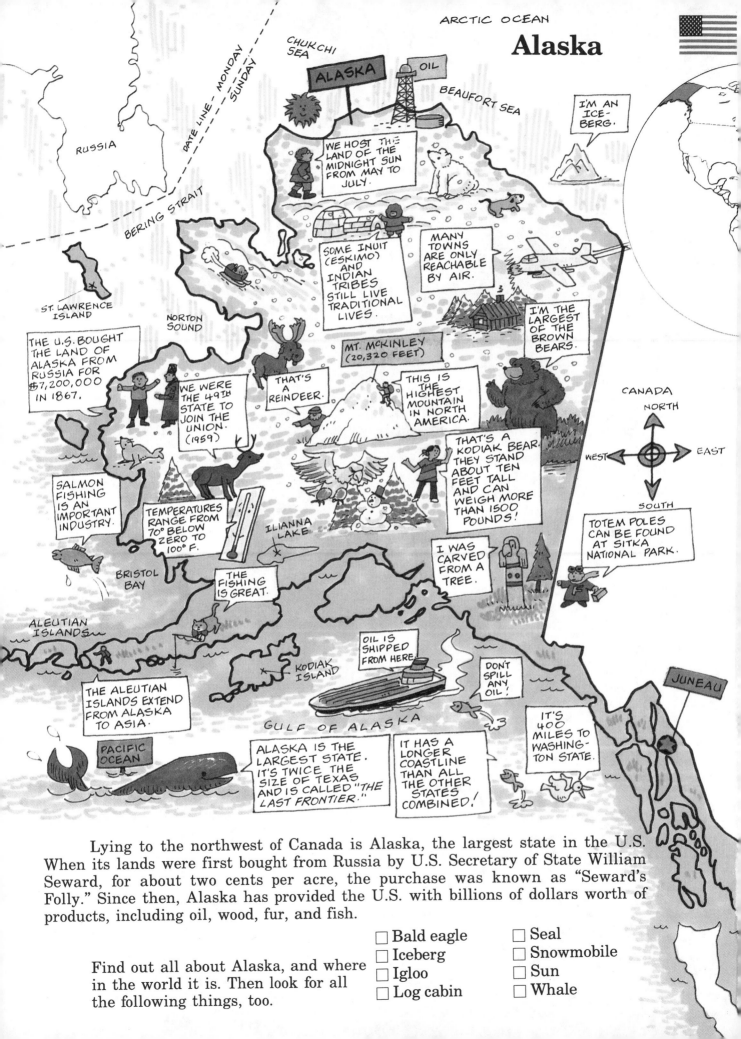

Lying to the northwest of Canada is Alaska, the largest state in the U.S. When its lands were first bought from Russia by U.S. Secretary of State William Seward, for about two cents per acre, the purchase was known as "Seward's Folly." Since then, Alaska has provided the U.S. with billions of dollars worth of products, including oil, wood, fur, and fish.

Find out all about Alaska, and where in the world it is. Then look for all the following things, too.

☐ Bald eagle
☐ Iceberg
☐ Igloo
☐ Log cabin
☐ Seal
☐ Snowmobile
☐ Sun
☐ Whale